The Step to Man

If you do not think about the future, you cannot have one.

—Galsworthy

Is man moving toward a new kind of life? Will the near future witness a unique transformation in the human condition, a transformation that will enable man to understand his destiny and to shape it? These questions, and their vital and absorbing answers, lie at the heart of *The Step to Man*.

This fascinating new book is the work of a biophysicist who is, at present, Associate Director of the Mental Health Research Institute at the University of Michigan. In it, he has drawn together a series of original, related essays on the evolving social and intellectual nature of man. The essays are concerned with what man is—and what he may become—and they touch upon almost every branch of human endeavor: science, education, history, social progress, philosophy, and literature. Offering us a fresh, dynamic overview of today's complex technological society, *The Step to Man* is a book that should be read by everyone interested in our changing evolutionary development.

See the back of this jacket for what prepublication reviewers have to say about the essays in this book.

The Step to Man

This book is concerned with
the evolving nature of man,
social and intellectual, what he is
and what he may become.

JOHN RADER PLATT

John Wiley & Sons, Inc.   *New York*   *London*   *Sydney*

Library of Congress Catalog Card Number: 66–17620
Printed in the United States of America

SECOND PRINTING, MARCH, 1967

Acknowledgments

The following chapters have appeared previously in the journals or books indicated and are reprinted by permission of the editors and publishers:

Where Will the Books Go?
   Horizon, September 1962, © American Heritage Publishing Co.
Strong Inference
   Science, 146, pp. 347–353, October 16, 1964.
Social Chain-Reactions
   Bulletin of the Atomic Scientists, November 1957 and November 1961.
Science as a Chain-Reaction
   Published in part in *Saturday Review,* September 2, 1961, under the title "On Thinking as a Chain-Reaction."
Research and Development for Social Problems
   Bulletin of the Atomic Scientists, June 1964.
The Step to Man
   Science, 149, pp. 607–613, August 6, 1965.

Contents

Structuring

*With microprinting, a library in every living room would
be able to contain the entire written record of humanity.*

Where Will the Books Go?

These essays are attempts to examine, from several points of
view, how the nature of man and his intellectual and social
organization is changing today, and what changes may be expected and hoped for and worked for in the next generation.

The best way is to start with some specific areas of change and
possible change. I have chosen two. The first deals with the implications of some new technical developments with respect to
the presentation and organization of human knowledge. The
second, to be discussed in the next chapter, will deal with intellectual developments in the organization of inference and
thought. Both of these are areas where dramatic changes are
already well under way and where the shape of the improvements ahead can already be discerned and reflected upon.

Physicists recently have been discussing a question that is going
to be of interest to every literate person: How small a book can
we make—and still read? Like many of the physicists' questions,
this one may seem merely microscopic and clever, but it bears
the seeds of immense social change.

Already, of course, we are in the early stages of the microbook
revolution.[1]* Business records, library copies of back issues of

* Notes and references will be found at the end of the book.

newspapers, thousands of Ph.D. dissertations, and many tens of thousands of "unpublished" and mimeographed research reports for government agencies are now on microfilm. This method gives a reduction of 40 to 60' times in the area of each page when it is photographed on standard 35-millimeter film. A second and higher degree of reduction is offered by microcards, which are coming into use in many libraries. On these, each page of a book is reduced in area by 500 to 1,000 times, so that the whole book can be printed on an ordinary-sized library catalogue card.

But why stop here? These reductions are still quite trivial compared to a third degree of reduction that we might get by going to the fundamental "optical limit." This is what is used in the "microdot" system, which has already been effective as an espionage device. In this scheme, a page of print is shrunk photographically down to the smallest size at which the individual letters can still be read through a high-powered optical microscope. The reduction in size from ordinary printing can be as much as 500 to 1,000 times in height and width, so that each letter and each page and each drawing and photograph is reduced in area by as much as one million times.

In this way, a whole sheet of spy data can be put into a "microdot" small enough to be pasted, say, on top of a single comma, or period, in an, otherwise, harmless text, where it may, often, pass unnoticed, by all except, perhaps, the most gimlet-eyed of censors.

ULTRAMICROSCOPIC BOOKS AND LIBRARIES

This microscopic printing was the limit, I said? Yes, but only the optical limit. A fourth degree of reduction is now possible that can go as far beyond this as the hydrogen bomb goes beyond the atomic bomb.

Five or six years ago, the theoretical physicist Richard P. Feynman of the California Institute of Technology gave a talk to the American Physical Society, which he called "There's Plenty of Room at the Bottom." [2] He pointed out that organic life is able to store its genetic information right at the ultimate molecular level, "printing" it in the form of long "coded" chains of atoms in the chromosomes. Why shouldn't we also try to approach this level with our intellectual information, by storing our words and pages at least near the limit of magnification of the electron-microscope? This would not be quite down to the level of molecular structure, but it could easily be "ultramicroscopic," say 100 times smaller—and perhaps in a few years 1,000 times smaller—than the limit of the optical microscope.

To make this suggestion concrete, Feynman proposed that we could "write" or "print" on a thin metal film by "etching" it away with a fine controlled "pencil" of electrons. A pencil 50 to 100 angstroms in diameter could write letters 300 to 500 angstroms high—that is, about one or two millionths of an inch. In Germany, recently, the physicist G. Möllenstedt proved the method would work and published an electron-microscopic picture of his initials—"G.Mö."—which he wrote on a metal film with an electronic pencil 80 angstroms wide.

With a little further work along these lines we could easily reach an electron-microscope reduction by 100,000 times in each dimension, so that an ordinary page of print would shrink to about 1 micron by 2 microns in area. One square millimeter— the area of the head of a pin, which for years has been the cliché of comparison in all such discussions—could then hold 1,000 books of 500 pages each. An ordinary sheet of paper represents about 20,000 of these millimeter areas, so that it would then hold all of the 20 million or so different books that are supposed to be contained in all the world's libraries. Or if we stack all these millimeter areas on top of each other, using metal films about 250 angstroms thick like those sometimes used in electron-microscope work, we would theoretically have a stack only about one-half millimeter high. This means, as Feynman emphasizes, that all the written knowledge in the world could then be stored inside the head of a single pin. An ultramicro-universalium. Hard to get at, perhaps, but what a pin!

And if, as he says, the library at Bogotá burned down, they wouldn't wail over their irreparable loss: they would simply say to the Library of Congress, send us another pin!

Actually, we may never have to compress our knowledge to this extent, but the possibilities offered are tantalizing. Are we now printing too many books and magazines, newspapers and reports, and forms in quintuplicate for filing? Many people think so. Robert Graves has even suggested that to recover our sanity we should abolish all paper and forbid anyone to have writing materials except poets. (He is a poet.) But the example of the pinhead library shows that we could have been publishing ten or a hundred times as much as we have been and our total production would still fit inside, let us say, the head of a thumbtack. At this rate, we could go on writing and printing for a million generations and still not even take up the volume of a big shelf of books today. When we begin to imitate the methods of organic life, we find out what the efficient storage of information really means.

And to Mr. Graves's selective whimsy, I would reply that each of us has his own kind of poetry, his own corner of human communication where he wants more, not less: the devout his devotional writings, the sociologist his correlations and insights, the physicist his potent texts. Put them all together and do they not add up simply to the sum of human discourse again?

Once you see that there is room for it all, you begin to wonder, indeed, if we should not publish much that we do not. In my universal library I want to have *everything*. *All* the letters in the attics, *all* the rejected manuscripts, *all* the "unpublished" reports, all the interoffice memos with ideas in them. Index them properly and cross-index them, so that we can find them when we want them—without wading through them when we do not!—and each may someday have its important little drop to contribute to the interrelated stream of human thought.

See, things are slipping into perspective already! It is only another cubic millimeter or so!

WILL WE EVER *LIKE* THEM?

The ultramicrobooks I have described are probably unnecessarily extreme for the moment, but I believe that the simpler microbooks, at our third, optical-microscope level of reduction, are already a foreseeable development.[3] I think it is interesting to note what becomes possible even at this level and how it may change our reading habits and attitudes. The conversion to microcopies is already coming fast because the sheer physical volume of full-sized "readable" books and documents is what makes them expensive to handle, to mail, or even to store on shelves for long periods. Any kind of microstorage cuts down on such costs, in library stacks as well as business files. The inconvenience of reading microcopies in a projection machine, or even the expense of making an occasional full-sized photographic copy, therefore becomes bearable for the masses of material not needed very often.

Microcopying is also being widely adopted as insurance. Much of the learning of the classical world has been lost to us through time and fire—much of Archimedes and most of Aeschylus and Sophocles, for example; and almost all of Sappho, who had been esteemed the greatest poet of the Western World for a thousand years. In those days, copying was by hand and expensive, and copies were few; and perhaps they all went up together when the library at Alexandria burned, with its hundreds of thousands of volumes, during Caesar's invasion, or when the remaining "pagan" books were put to the torch in the time of Saint Gregory Nazianzen. Low-cost microprinting, by which unique documents and even whole libraries can be put in a small space and protected, promises to make the preservation of our learning much more certain. A pin in the lapel of a simple tourist may be able to cross all borders and survive all bookburnings.

The trouble is that the advantages of microstorage are institutional, while its disadvantages are personal. We have come to enjoy the sensory pleasures we have associated for the past few hundred years with the life of the intellect—the pleasures of browsing among the shelves, of handling real books and smelling the print, of flipping through the pages to look at the pictures or the endings, or even of turning down the page corners or writing vigorous rebuttals in the margins. Our big libraries have already made bookreading a formal chore, with their forbidding circulation desks and their elaborate call-card systems and long delays. Some of us may fear that if we now have to read microbooks only on projection screens, the literate pleasures will vanish completely. It may be research, but it is not *reading*.

Actually, of course, the libraries will continue to have space for about as many full-sized books as they ever had. What microcopies will do is permit libraries to add a great deal of rarer material to their collections—for those who are interested in seeing it even in microform—without having to expand the buildings. Can any library-lover object to that? What is needed may simply be some new inventions, some improvements in projectors and film-handling, so that microfilm could be projected on a well-lit, well-focused screen in front of a comfortable chair, with simple controls at hand for "selecting books" and "turning the pages." If such a "microbook reader" were really pleasant and easy to use, every home would begin to want one and every library would want dozens; and we all might begin to prefer getting our books, and reading them, in the light, inexpensive microfilm form.

In history, we have gone from picture hieroglyphs, and cuneiform writing with a stylus on clay and stone tablets, to writing with ink on papyrus rolls; then to vellum books about 2,000 years ago; to paper books about 1,200 years ago; to printing with movable type about 500 years ago; and in the last few decades to many diversified methods of printing—and photocopying. Is any one of these historical methods uniquely precious in the physical form it takes? Probably each has seemed so, to a generation brought up to respect it. I can imagine a time when the Minoan palace warehouses were bursting at the seams with baked clay records, but when a dedicated record-keeper nonetheless would show a good deal of resistance to the new papyrus scrolls. With their long inscriptions written in streaks of fading ink paste on a thin rolled-up inflammable sheet, they must have seemed terribly complicated, impermanent, inaccessible, and expensive to a man accustomed to the simplicity and solidity of clay tablets.

We feel much the same way about microfilm today. But we must remember that what is precious is not the physical "artifacts" of a system of writing but the "mentifacts," the human communications they contain. When our books change into new forms, children brought up to love the things of the mind will come to treat these forms with the same feelings of respect, familiarity, and pleasure that we have had for the old ones.

HUMAN KNOWLEDGE ON THE DESK TOP

And then we will have real microlibraries. At the optical-microscope level of reduction, all those 20 million books in all the world's libraries could be put on a desk top, or in a cabinet beside the record player. It would be worth spending a lot for. The present microfilm and microcard reductions may not have gone quite far enough to open up the big market that this smaller size could reach. Are you a student? A doctor? Do you need some obscure Polish journal, an old book, or a patent? You need not go to a special University collection or to the John Crerar Library. Look right on your desk. The journal ceases to be obscure, and specialized human knowledge ceases to seem inaccessible.

A few words about the conceivable dimensions and possible mechanisms and costs of such a development may help convince us how close it is to being practical and profitable. With an optical-microscope system permitting a reduction in area of about one million times, our 20 million volumes could be photocopied into 20 average volumes, about half the size of a standard encyclopedia. (Even if the copies were made 10 or 20 times larger in area, to simplify technical problems such as the optical tolerances and the heat of the projector, they could still fit into a big desk or bookcase.) Each sheet in our hypothetical 20 volumes might contain, say, 2,000 books of 500 pages each; and each volume 500 such sheets, or one million books; with a total of 10,000 sheets in all the 20 volumes, about the number in an encyclopedia today.

We would want to keep the sheets inside a cabinet, of course, to avoid dust and fingerprints; and it would be extremely important to keep them in proper order, indexed to some standard system like the Library of Congress system, so that anyone could locate quickly the sheet he wanted and the book he wanted on it. (At the level of reduction I am talking about, a book would be about the size of a single letter on an ordinary page. Is one particular letter so hard to find?) In more expensive installations, a mechanical selector like those in jukeboxes might be used for selecting a sheet and positioning it under the projection microscope automatically when its number is dialed; this would prevent disarrangement and damage from handling the sheets.

The kind of sheets I am talking about would not necessarily be sheets printed in rectangular array like book pages, but might instead be strips of tape, rolled or folded, or perhaps disks, according to what is mechanically simplest. The breaking up of the linear line of thought into "pages" and "lines" of print has always depended on the technology of book construction. It was different in scrolls and books, and it may be different again in microbooks as they become perfected. Someday, also, it might be technologically simpler or more flexible to have electronic scanning of the microbooks rather than optical projection.[4] Scanners that could project a page onto any television screen in the house; in the living-room, the play-room, or the bedroom, may be in the offing. One can imagine our reader of the future in his easy chair or lying in bed, with the control box at his fingertips, roaming on the screen in front of him, anywhere he wishes in the world's literature. There will always be a book for insomnia, something more real, more bizarre, more concentrated, or more far-flung than anything the ordinary television drama can ever offer; and he won't have to go and get the book during library hours; and he won't have to return it in two weeks.

What would such a dream library cost? Probably a few hundred dollars for a projection microscope, at medical-microscope or slide-projector prices. Probably a few hundred dollars for the 10,000 microprinted sheets, if they were "contact prints" made from master sheets, at costs comparable to present costs for contact photocopies. (The fine-grained film costs more, but mass production should bring it down.) Probably a few hundred dollars per user—if there were, say, 200,000 or more professional users—for copying all the 20 million books onto the master sheets, at present copying rates. Perhaps a thousand dollars or so for a special storage rack with a mechanical selector, allowing for the fact that such a mechanism must be delicate and precise, but also for the fact that there should be economies in mass production.

And certainly we should allow comparable sums, maybe a thousand dollars or two, for royalties and copyrights to permit recent and current books to be microprinted in these desk libraries. Add it all up and if these "iffy" estimates are not too far off, the total cost per Universal Library might then be in the three-to-six thousand dollar range.

This could cost far less and be worth more to many of us, and might have more buyers, than those desk-top electronic computers that have been talked about for years. The sum is not much more than many students and professional people pay for books and journals over, say, a twenty-year period, and is much less than the cost of a reading room or study in a new house, so that such a library system might be built into many houses and apartments, much as high-fidelity systems are built in today. My guess is that there might be more than half a million doctors, lawyers, engineers, scientists, and teachers in the United States who might buy such a microlibrary on the installment plan at this price. After all, it would contain in one package all those expensive medical books, all the texts and back volumes of scientific journals, all the encyclopedias; and everything else, too. Plus all the library apparatus of catalogues, guides, and indexes to help find things in all the other books you would now own.

At this price, a desk-top library, or several of them, would be a "must" for newspaper offices, publishers, industrial companies with patent or reference problems; and every grammar and high school and library over the world. However many the initial number of users, they would grow over the years as the easy looking-up of answers of all kinds began to be taken for granted. To finance the initial costs, such a system might be developed in stages, starting with technical literature, where the first users might be willing to pay more and where royalty and copyright problems might be less serious; the cost of completing the humanities and historical sections might then be relatively small. From a national point of view, even, the value of having a complete Library of Congress within reach of every student, teacher, and scientist might be comparable to the value of our great highway systems, and the initial development might be deserving of similar government support. These thoughts suggest that a more careful cost and market analysis might be worth making, by photographic and microscope manufacturers, publishers, libraries, government agencies, and scientists, to see whether complete microlibraries of this kind may not represent a billion dollar market simply awaiting development.

Where will the books go? Where *everybody* can read them—which is where they have always belonged.

TOTALITY AND SELECTION

At this point I must make a confession. I have spent this much space in speculating on these technical and commercial aspects, not because I am so much interested in the details, which might be quite different from what I have imagined, but because the desk-top library is an especially graphic image to keep in mind in trying to get a real feeling for some of the problems connected with the scope and growth of human knowledge. It is equivalent to taking us up to a high place from which we can see it all. Just as when we first get a view of our whole city from a nearby hill or from a plane, we suddenly see the relations of the parts and the true size of man's intellectual achievements at a single glance—something we saw before only house by house and street by street.

It is only when you consider seriously the possibility of owning, of having at your fingertips, and being able to read in your own chair, all the world's literature and learning, that you can actually begin to think of this knowledge as a whole and see what our future attitude toward it may be like as we as a race grow more mature. The actual users of microlibraries, when they finally do come along, will grow up in the daily presence of this totality. They will be reminded continually of just what is before them, and of how complex it is; and as a result will begin to use it in a masterful way almost unimaginable for our present-day scholars, buried as they are in some corner of it, surrounded by their physical acres of library stacks.

Consider how your own reactions might change, step by step, if you were a scholar or layman in 1970 or 2070, as you began to get used to having at hand, all the time, anything you wanted to know that human beings know. When you get your first Universal Library, very likely you will hurry to dip into it here and there—to find all the entrancing and unavailable books you have not read before. Probably for a while you will also be fascinated in looking at all the subjects—microbrowsing—on any sheet you open to, and reading samples of the ones that look interesting or have interesting pictures. This is the way a bright twelve-year-old acts when his family gets its first adult encylopedia, and it is not a bad way of exploring and getting the feel of how to use the system. But after a few days you will come to realize, as he does, that at almost every point the material is too hard or too trivial or not really interesting, and that certainly there is too much of it. And you will begin to use the library more and more selectively and purposefully, to read specific things only when you are referred to them, or when a question comes up, or when your interest is aroused.

At about this point, with the microlibrary, you will also begin to realize something new: namely, how fast additional human discourse is coming in. The 300,000 or so new titles per year that the Library of Congress now adds to its stacks will double our 20 Universal Volumes in a generation or so. And they do not even include all the material published under old titles—the magazines and newspapers and the 300,000 new scientific articles per year, with 600 new medical articles every day. All this adds up to a new Addition Sheet with the contents of 2,000 ordinary-sized books every day or two. Not much in terms of the pinhead library we talked about earlier, but staggering in individual terms. When the Addition Sheets begin to arrive regularly in the mail, you will be continually reminded not only that you cannot read everything ever written, but that you cannot even keep up with one-thousandth of the new material being added every day. And this is as true for the scientist, the philosopher, or the scholar as it is for the layman.

We begin, then, to wonder seriously: How much can an intelligent man know, and how much should he try to know, of previous or current human learning?

From our present vantage point we see that the number of books a man can digest in a lifetime is very small. A vigorous editor or book critic may scan four books in a day, or perhaps 1,000 a year. But for reading and digesting articles or books worth reading, the rate is much lower, and the average literate adult probably cannot absorb more than two to four books per week, even including those in his own specialty. If we say 160 books per year for 50 years, or 8,000 books, we will be describing a very bookish lifetime.

What it adds up to is four of the microprinted sheets out of the 10,000 in our Universal Library.

We realize suddenly that even the men most famous in history for their learning could not have known from their own reading more than a microscopic fraction of the lore of their times. The supposition that there was a time when a man could "know everything" is one of those Great Men myths that worshippers use to make their contemporaries seem small and themselves seem excusable.

The wisest philosophers, Socrates and Kant, probably fell short of reading their 8,000 books; they were too busy thinking. (And in Socrates' day, 8,000 would still have been only a tiny fraction of the hundreds of thousands of books that were in the Greek libraries.) The "universal men," Bacon, Leonardo, and Goethe, did not have time for their 8,000; they were too busy working. Even the great encyclopedists, Aristotle and Diderot, could scarcely have had time for their 8,000, in view of the time that they must have spent at their own writing.

Most of us today are omnivorous readers—or scanners—of newspapers, magazines, current books, and even encyclopedias. We were brought up reading. We were brought up to think it is good, and it is. Indeed I suspect that millions of us read more than any of the great men of the past. But do we profit more from it?

The trouble is that we were not brought up selecting. This is the wisdom of the wise men; not that they knew, but that they chose. It is a wisdom anyone can practice. We are harassed and hypnotized by print. But it is time to stop being passive about how we spend our minds. Are you not frightened by the thought of that long path of newsprint unrolling ahead of you down the years? Put some other kind of print beside your coffee cup. After you have read some of the newspaper, like an intelligent citizen, read something that touches your real interests more closely, like an intelligent human being.

There is no need to be all grim and serious about this, of course. We all have different jobs to do, and different intellectual hungers, and we all need different kinds of things to read at different times; from whodunits to history, from *Pogo* to the *Perennial Philosophy*. Often, nothing will restore our sanity like gales of laughter. Nevertheless, it is salutary to ask yourself when you next reach for a book, Is this one of the 8,000—or the

4,000 or the 2,000—I really want to build into my life? It clarifies your choices wonderfully.

And why not 4,000 or 2,000? Since the most a man can read is trivial anyway in comparison with the total human library, why not enrich yourself by spending more time and thought on just the 80 per year or the 40 per year that are most relevant to your own condition and purposes? The original references, not the texts. (You could think, in between.) The original authors, not the critical reviews. (You could live, in between.) The original poets, not the discussions of poetry. (You could write, in between.)

THE NEED FOR JUDGMENT

All this is a considerable oversimplification, of course. How does a man know what he would profit most from, when choosing his reading? He must get advice and read reviews and decide whose judgment he trusts. How does he know where to find it? By looking it up in the indexing systems and hoping they are accurate and complete. How does he know what his own interests really are? Ah, there's the problem. By self-exploration, in the light of the challenges he gets from being interested in what he reads. It is all a cumulative problem, with another step in self-development after every round. But we see that evaluation, selection, and indexing are all intertwined; and the user of the desk-top library will be reminded of that every day.

The indexing problem is of the greatest concern today, especially with the flood of new material and the masses of micro-filmed documents, most of them hard to classify by the old categories. Many librarians, scientists, and government agencies are trying to invent more satisfactory indexing systems that will keep all these bits of information from getting lost through inadequate indexing or cross-indexing. It all makes me think we may be approaching a time when scholars and scientists will find it convenient to memorize the index numbers of their own interests, and to arrange that only the papers and documents will be sent to them whose index numbers coincide with theirs. "I'm 437 and 411.293. What are you?" Today the doctor can flip through his medical journal when it arrives in the mail, stopping at a familiar name or subject or at a figure that interests him. How long before he can scan as quickly and rewardingly a microfilm strip of the same journal, or of all the medical journals? Just as long as it takes for us to begin indexing and cross-indexing articles in advance, so that he can turn instantly to what interests him.

But even if this problem could be solved, we would still have to evaluate. The outsider cannot know what is important and what is trivial or wrong in the books of category 411.293, except by getting the evaluations of one or two insiders; and he will still have to decide for himself whether their judgment is reliable. Every time we use other men's knowledge, we face this question, whether we are conscious of it or not. Can we doubt that even the young Socrates was confronted by it when he acquired, from his teachers or from his own experience and judgment, his ideas of what problems *not* to be interested in and what books *not* to read?

When we look down at the world's complete knowledge, we see with sudden and total clarity that what an education can give us is not any mere accumulation of reading, no matter how vast, but relationships and judgment. A man who has well-educated himself knows how the different parts of the body of knowledge fit together, even though he cannot know all the details except in one or two tiny corners. He knows which parts are generally relevant to his interests. He decides for himself when to read the Gee-Whiz reporters or the digesters and when to leave their tidbits untouched. He knows what he wants to explore more carefully or contribute to, and what he does not. But even in areas outside his own competence, where he must to some degree trust the experts and evaluators—as Socrates and Aristotle and every other philosopher or synthesizer has had to trust them—he can still tell sloppy reasoning from sound, and to some degree judge these various experts for himself.

Those universal men who were supposed to know something about every science are not really celebrated for the completeness of their information but for this kind of selection and comparison, judgment and insight. Their learning was microscopic, compared to all human learning, as it always will be; their judgment was large, as it always can be.

The reason we do not have such men in our time is that we lack confidence in our choice and judgment. We think we can make up for it by specializing and devouring. As scholars and scientists and philosophers and teachers, we get started in one specialty and often go on all our lives without ever looking around. We feel surrounded and small, and we talk about being overwhelmed by the sweep and complexity of modern knowledge. In every university we see scholars bloated from trying to gulp too much, 14 hours a day, until they cease to be men at all. As one of our wits has said, The thirst for knowledge should have a sphincter on it. I have often heard scientists say, "There is just too much!" But we need not feel this way any more than the scholars of old; what one man can know is not significantly smaller now than it was then, compared to the vast unknown total. A universal man is simply a man who chooses and combines and refuses to be overwhelmed.

THE BEGINNINGS OF A BRAIN

I think that if we ever come to have widespread micro-libraries, adequately indexed, with the whole world of learning and letters immediately at hand, this universal attitude will also become widespread. Without it, in fact, no one will be able to employ a universal microlibrary effectively. Some people will use the library to read for pleasure—almost everyone, let us hope. Some will use it to look up scholarly, technical, or managerial answers; some, to find points of departure for their own new contributions to knowledge. But I think all of these users will acquire an air of intellectual comprehension and assurance, like a man with a brain who knows what he is about.

For the microlibrary will begin to have some of the coherent qualities of a brain. If all our knowledge can be brought together in a familiar system within everyone's reach, the increase in the intelligence and effectiveness of our behavior should be astonishing. The world's knowledge, kept up to date, will become a closer and closer adjunct to all kinds of decision making and action. The microscopic library, with its interrelated information instantly accessible, will make possible a new awareness of relations and consequences, a widespread and rapid interplay of human ideas and inventions, and a directness of collective decision such as we could not have imagined without it. Because it is small and closely knit, delays and uncertainties will be reduced as they are in a real brain. In our use of it we can therefore begin to approach the unity and directness of our own complex biological decision-making and memory system, with its similarly interrelated and microscopic neuron elements, similarly packed in a compact space, within a single skull. Microlibraries would be a memory and the beginnings of a universal brain for the whole human race.

Certain systematic methods of scientific thinking may produce much more rapid progress than others.

Strong Inference

Scientists tend to keep up a polite fiction that all science is equal. Outside of the misguided opponent whose work we happen to be refuting at the time, we speak as though every scientist's field and methods of study are as good as every other scientist's, and perhaps a little better. This keeps us all cordial when it comes to recommending each other for government grants.

But I think anyone who looks at the matter closely will agree that some fields of science are moving forward very much faster than others, perhaps an order of magnitude faster, if numbers could be put on such estimates. The discoveries leap from the headlines—and they are real advances in complex and difficult subjects, like molecular biology and high-energy physics. As Alvin Weinberg says, "Hardly a month goes by without a stunning success in molecular biology being reported in the *Proceedings of the National Academy of Sciences*." [1]

Why should there be such rapid advances in some fields rather than others? I think the usual explanations that we tend to think of—such as the tractability of the subject, or the quality or education of the men drawn into it, or the size of research contracts—are important but inadequate. I have begun to believe that the primary factor in scientific advance is an intellectual one. These rapidly moving fields are fields where a particular method of doing scientific research is systematically used and taught, an accumulative method of inductive inference that is so effective that I think it should be given the name of "strong inference." I believe it is important to examine this method, its use and history and rationale, to see whether other groups and individuals might learn to adopt it profitably in their own scientific and intellectual work.

In its separate elements, strong inference is just the simple and old-fashioned method of inductive inference that goes back to Francis Bacon. The steps are familiar to every college student and are practiced, off and on, by every scientist. The difference comes in their systematic application. *Strong inference consists of applying the following steps to every problem in science, formally and explicitly and regularly:*

(1) *devising alternative hypotheses;*

(2) *devising a crucial experiment* (or several of them), *with alternative possible outcomes*, each of which will, as nearly as possible, *exclude one or more of the hypotheses;*

(3) *carrying out the experiment* so as to get a clean result; and

(1') *recycling* the procedure, making subhypotheses or sequential hypotheses to refine the possibilities that remain; and so on.

It is like climbing a tree. At the first fork, we choose—or in this case, "nature" or the experimental outcome chooses—to go to the right branch or the left; at the next fork, to go left or right; and so on. There are similar branch points in a "conditional computer program" where the next move depends on the result of the last calculation. And there is a "conditional inductive tree" or "logical tree" of this kind written out in detail in many first-year chemistry books, in the table of steps for qualitative analysis of an unknown sample, where the student is led through a real problem of consecutive inference. Add Reagent A; if you get a red precipitate, it is subgroup Alpha and you filter and add Reagent B; if not, you add the other Reagent B'; and so on.

On any new problem, of course, inductive inference is not as simple and certain as deduction, because it involves reaching out into the unknown. Steps (1) and (2) require intellectual inventions, which must be cleverly chosen so that hypothesis, experiment, outcome, and exclusion will be related in a rigorous syllogism; and the question of how to generate such inventions is one which has been extensively discussed elsewhere.[2,3] What the formal schema reminds us to do is to try to make these inventions, to take the next step, to proceed to the next fork, without dawdling or getting tied up in irrelevancies.

It is clear why this makes for rapid and powerful progress. For exploring the unknown, there is no faster method; this is the minimum sequence of steps. Any conclusion that is not an exclusion is insecure and must be rechecked. Any delay in recycling to the next set of hypotheses is only a delay. Strong inference, and the logical tree it generates, are to inductive reasoning what the syllogism is to deductive reasoning, in offering a regular method for reaching firm inductive conclusions one after the other as rapidly as possible.

"But what is so novel about this?," someone will say. This is *the* method of science and always has been; why give it a special name? The reason is that many of us have almost forgotten it. Science is now an everyday business. Equipment, calculations, and lectures become ends in themselves. How many of us write down our alternatives and crucial experiments every day, focusing on the *exclusion* of a hypothesis? We may write our scientific papers so that it looks as if we had steps (1), (2), and (3) in mind all along. But in between, we do busywork. We become "method-oriented" rather than "problem-oriented." We say we prefer to "feel our way" toward generalizations. We fail to teach our students how to sharpen up their inductive inferences. And we do not realize the added power that the regular and explicit use of alternative hypotheses and sharp exclusions could give us at every step of our research.

The difference between the average scientist's informal methods and the methods of the strong-inference users is somewhat like the difference between a gasoline engine that fires occasionally and one that fires in steady sequence. If our motorboat engines were as erratic as our deliberate intellectual efforts, most of us would not get home for supper.

MOLECULAR BIOLOGY

The new molecular biology is a field in which the application of this systematic method of inference has become widespread and effective. It is a complex field; yet a succession of crucial experiments over the past decade has given us a surprisingly detailed understanding of hereditary mechanisms and the control of enzyme formation and protein synthesis.

The logical structure shows in every experiment. In 1953 James Watson and Francis Crick proposed that the DNA molecule—the "hereditary substance" in a cell—is a long two-stranded helical molecule.[4] This theory suggested a number of alternatives for crucial test. Do the two strands of the helix stay together when a cell divides or do they separate? Matthew Meselson and Franklin Stahl used an ingenious isotope-density-labeling technique which showed that they separate.[5] Does the DNA helix always have two strands or can it have three, as atomic models suggest? Alexander Rich showed it can have either, depending on the ionic concentration.[6] These are the kind of experiments that John Dalton would have liked, where the combining entities are not atoms but long macromolecular strands.

To take a different sort of question, is the "genetic map"— showing the statistical relationship of different genetic characteristics in recombination experiments—a one-dimensional map like the DNA molecule, that is, a linear map, as T. H. Morgan proposed in 1911; or does it have two-dimensional loops or branches? Seymour Benzer showed that his hundreds of fine microgenetic experiments on bacteria would only fit the mathematical matrix for the one-dimensional case.[7]

But of course, selected crucial experiments of this kind can be found in every field. The real difference in molecular biology is that formal inductive inference is so systematically practiced and taught. On any given morning at the Laboratory of Molecular Biology in Cambridge, England, the blackboards of Francis Crick or Sidney Brenner will commonly be found covered with logical trees. On the top line will be the hot new result just up from the laboratory or just in by letter or rumor. On the next line will be two or three alternative explanations, or a little list of "What he did wrong." Underneath will be a series of suggested experiments or controls that can reduce the number of possibilities. And so on. The tree grows during the day as one man or another comes in and argues about why one of the experiments wouldn't work, or how it should be changed.

The strong-inference attitude is evident just in the style and language in which the papers are written. For example, in analyzing theories of antibody formation, Joshua Lederberg gives a list of nine propositions "subject to denial," discussing which ones would be "most vulnerable to experimental test." [8]

The papers of the French leaders Francois Jacob and Jacques Monod are also celebrated for their high "logical density," with paragraph after paragraph of linked "inductive syllogisms." But the style is widespread. Start with the first paper in the *Journal of Molecular Biology* for 1964, and you immediately find: "Our conclusions . . . might be invalid if . . . (1) . . . (2) . . . or (3). . . . We shall describe experiments which eliminate these alternatives. . . ." [9] The average physicist, chemist, or scientist in any field accustomed to less closely reasoned articles and less sharply stated inferences, will find it a salutary experience to dip into this journal almost at random.

RESISTANCE TO ANALYTICAL METHODOLOGY

This analytical approach to biology has sometimes become almost a crusade, because it arouses so much resistance in many scientists who have grown up in a more relaxed and diffuse tradition. At the 1958 Conference on Biophysics at Boulder, there was a dramatic confrontation between the two points of view. Leo Szilard said: "The problems of how enzymes are induced, of how proteins are synthesized, of how antibodies are formed, are closer to solution than is generally believed. If you do stupid experiments, and finish one a year, it can take 50 years. But if you stop doing experiments for a little while and *think* how proteins can possibly be synthesized, there are only about 5 different ways, not 50! And it will take only a few experiments to distinguish these."

One of the young men added: "It is essentially the old question: How *small* and *elegant* an experiment can you perform?"

These comments upset a number of those present. An electron

microscopist said, "Gentlemen, this is off the track. This is philosophy of science."

Szilard retorted, "I was not quarreling with third-rate scientists: I was quarreling with first-rate scientists."

A physical chemist hurriedly asked, "Are we going to take the official photograph before lunch or after lunch?"

But this did not deflect the dispute. A distinguished cell biologist rose and said, "No two cells give the same properties. Biology is the science of heterogeneous systems. . . ." And he added privately, "You know there are *scientists;* and there are people in science who are just working with these oversimplified model systems—DNA chains and *in vitro* systems—who are not doing science at all. We need their auxiliary work: They build apparatus, they make minor studies, but they are not scientists."

To which Cy Levinthal of M.I.T. said: "Well, there are two kinds of biologist, those who are looking to see if there is one thing that can be understood, and those who keep saying it is very complicated and that nothing can be understood. . . . You must study the *simplest* system you think has the properties you are interested in."

As they were leaving the meeting, one man could be heard muttering, "What does Szilard expect me to do—shoot myself?"

Any criticism or challenge to consider changing our methods strikes, of course, at all our ego defenses. But in this case the analytical method offers the possibility of such great increases in effectiveness that it is unfortunate that it cannot be regarded more often as a challenge to learning rather than as a challenge to combat. Many of the recent triumphs in molecular biology have, in fact, been achieved on just such "oversimplified model systems," very much along the analytical lines laid down in the 1958 discussion. They have not fallen to the kind of men who justify themselves by saying, "No two cells are alike," regardless of how true that may ultimately be. The triumphs are, in fact, triumphs of a new way of thinking.

HIGH-ENERGY PHYSICS

This analytical thinking is rare, but it is by no means restricted to the new biology. High-energy physics is another field where the logic of exclusions is obvious, even in the newspaper accounts. For example, in the famous discovery of C. N. Yang and T. D. Lee, the question that was asked was: Do the fundamental particles conserve mirror symmetry or "parity" in certain reactions, or do they not? The crucial experiments were suggested; within a few months they were done; and conservation of parity was found to be excluded. Richard Garwin and Leon Lederman and Marcel Weinrich did one of the crucial experiments. It was thought of one evening at suppertime; by midnight they had rearranged the apparatus for it; and by 4 A.M. they had picked up the predicted pulses showing the nonconservation of parity.[10] The phenomena had just been waiting, so to speak, for the explicit formulation of the alternative hypotheses.

The theorists in this field take pride in trying to predict new properties or new particles explicitly enough that if they are not found, the theories will fall. As the biologist W. A. H. Rushton has said, "A theory which cannot be mortally endangered cannot be alive." [11] Murray Gell-Mann and Yuval Ne'eman recently used the particle-grouping which they call "The Eightfold Way" to predict a missing particle, the Omega-Minus, which was then looked for and found.[12] But one alternative branch of the theory would predict a particle with one-third the usual electronic charge, and it was not found in the experiments, so this branch had to be rejected.

The logical tree is so much a part of high-energy physics that some stages of it are commonly built, in fact, into the electronic coincidence circuits that detect the particles and trigger the bubble-chamber photographs. Each kind of particle should give a different kind of pattern in the electronic counters, and the circuits can be set to exclude or include whatever types of events are desired. If the distinguishing criteria are sequential, they may even run through a complete logical tree in a microsecond or so. This electronic pre-analysis, like human pre-analysis of alternative outcomes, speeds up progress by sharpening the criteria. It eliminates hundreds of thousands of the irrelevant pictures that formerly had to be scanned; and when carried to its limit, a few output pulses hours apart may be enough to signal the existence of the antiproton or the fall of a theory.

I think the emphasis on strong inference in the two fields I have mentioned has been partly the result of personal leadership, such as that of the classical geneticists in molecular biology, or Szilard with his "Midwest Chowder and Bacteria Society" at Chicago in 1948–1950, or Max Delbrück with his summer courses in phage genetics at Cold Spring Harbor. But it is also partly due to the nature of the fields themselves. Biology, with its vast informational detail and complexity, is a "high-information" field where years and decades can easily be wasted on the usual type of "low-information" observations or experiments if one does not think carefully in advance about what the most important and conclusive experiments would be. And in high-energy physics, both the "information-flux" of particles from the new accelerators and the million-dollar costs of operation have forced a similar analytical approach. It pays to have a top-notch group debate every experiment ahead of time; and the habit spreads throughout the field.

INDUCTION AND MULTIPLE HYPOTHESES

Historically, I think there have been two main contributions to the development of a satisfactory strong-inference method. The first is that of Francis Bacon.[13] He wanted a "surer method" of "finding out nature" than either the logic-chopping or all-inclusive theories of the time or the laudable but crude attempts to make inductions "by simple enumeration." He did not merely urge experiments, as some suppose; he showed the fruitfulness of interconnecting theory and experiment so that the one checked the other. Of the many inductive procedures he suggested, the most important, I think, was the conditional inductive tree, which proceeded from alternative hypotheses (possible "causes," as he calls them) through crucial experiments ("Instances of the Fingerpost") to exclusion of some alternatives and adoption of what is left ("establishing axioms"). His instances of the Fingerpost are explicitly at the forks in the logical tree, "borrowing the term from the fingerposts which are set up where roads part, to indicate the several directions."

Many of his crucial experiments proposed in Book Two of *The New Organon* are still fascinating. For example, in order to decide whether the weight of a body is due to its "inherent nature," as some had said, or is due to the attraction of the earth, which would decrease with distance, he proposes comparing the rate of a pendulum clock and a spring clock and then lifting them from the earth to the top of a tall steeple. He concludes that if the pendulum clock on the steeple "goes more slowly than it did on account of the diminished virtue of its weights . . . we may take the attraction of the mass of the earth as the cause of weight."

Here was a method that could separate off the empty theories!

Bacon said the inductive method could be learned by anybody, just like learning to "draw a straighter line or more perfect circle . . . with the help of a ruler or a pair of compasses." "My way of discovering sciences goes far to level men's wit and leaves but little to individual excellence, because it performs everything by the surest rules and demonstrations." Even occasional mistakes would not be fatal. "Truth will sooner come out from error than from confusion."

It is easy to see why young minds leaped to try it.

Nevertheless, there is a difficulty with this method. As Bacon emphasizes, it is necessary to make "exclusions." He says, "The induction which is to be available for the discovery and demonstration of sciences and arts, must analyze nature by proper rejections and exclusions; and then, after a sufficient number of negatives, come to a conclusion on the affirmative instances." "[To man] it is granted only to proceed at first by negatives, and at last to end in affirmatives after exclusion has been exhausted."

Or, as the philosopher Karl Popper says today, there is no such thing as proof in science—because some later alternative explanation may be as good or better—so that science advances only by disproofs. There is no point in making hypotheses that are not falsifiable, because such hypotheses do not say anything; "it must be possible for an empirical scientific system to be refuted by experience." [14]

The difficulty is that disproof is a hard doctrine. If you have a hypothesis and I have another hypothesis, one of them must evidently be eliminated. The scientist seems to have no choice but to be either soft-headed or disputatious. Perhaps this is why so many tend to resist the strong analytical approach—and why some great scientists are so disputatious.

Fortunately, it seems to me that this difficulty can be removed by the use of a second great intellectual invention, the "method of multiple hypotheses," which is what was needed to round out the Baconian scheme. This is a method that was put forward by T. C. Chamberlin,[15] the great American geologist, who is perhaps best known today for his contribution to the Chamberlin-Moulton hypothesis of the origin of the solar system.

Chamberlin says our trouble is that when we make a single hypothesis, we become attached to it.

The moment one has offered an original explanation for a phenomenon which seems satisfactory, that moment affection for his intellectual child springs into existence, and as the explanation grows into a definite theory his parental affections cluster about his offspring and it grows more and more dear to him. . . . There springs up also unwittingly a pressing of the theory to make it fit the facts and a pressing of the facts to make them fit the theory. . . .

To avoid this grave danger, the method of multiple working hypotheses is urged. It differs from the simple working hypothesis in that it distributes the effort and divides the affections. . . . Each hypothesis suggests its own criteria, its own means of proof, its own method of developing the truth, and if a group of hypotheses encompass the subject on all sides, the total outcome of means and of methods is full and rich.

Chamberlin thinks the method "leads to certain distinctive habits of mind" and is of prime value in education. "When faithfully followed for a sufficient time, it develops a mode of thought of its own kind which may be designated the habit of complex thought. . . ."

This charming paper deserves to be reprinted in some more accessible journal today where it could be required reading for every graduate student—and for every professor.

It seems to me that Chamberlin has hit on the explanation—and the cure—for many of our problems in the sciences. The conflict and exclusion of alternatives that is necessary to sharp inductive inference has been all too often a conflict between men, each with his single Ruling Theory. But whenever each man begins to have multiple working hypotheses, it becomes purely a conflict between ideas. It becomes much easier then for each of us to aim every day at conclusive disproofs—at *strong* inference—without either reluctance or combativeness. In fact, when there are multiple hypotheses which are not anyone's "personal property" and when there are crucial experiments to test them, the daily life in the laboratory takes on an interest and excitement it never had, and the students can hardly wait to get to work to see how the detective story will come out. It seems to me that this is the reason for the development of those "distinctive habits of mind" and the "complex thought" that Chamberlin described, the reason for the sharpness, the excitement, the zeal, the teamwork—yes, even international team-work—in molecular biology and high-energy physics today. What else could be so effective?

When multiple hypotheses become coupled to strong inference, the scientific search becomes an emotional powerhouse as well as an intellectual one.

Unfortunately, I think there are other areas of science today that are sick by comparison, because they have forgotten the necessity for alternative hypotheses and disproof. Each man has only one branch—or none—on the logical tree, and it twists at random without ever coming to the need for a crucial decision at any point. We can see from the external symptoms that there is something scientifically wrong. The Frozen Method. The Eternal Surveyor. The Never Finished. The Great Man With a Single Hypothesis. The Little Club of Dependents. The Vendetta. The All-Encompassing Theory Which Can Never Be Falsified.

Some cynics tell a story, which may be apocryphal, about the theoretical chemist who explained to his class,

"And thus we see that the C–Cl bond is longer in the first compound than in the second because the per cent of ionic character is smaller."

A voice from the back of the room said, "But Professor X., according to the table, the C–Cl bond is shorter in the first compound."

"Oh, is it?" said the professor. ". . . Well, that's still easy to understand, because the double-bond character is higher in that compound."

To the extent that this kind of story is accurate, a "theory" of this sort is not a theory at all because it does not exclude anything. It predicts everything, and therefore does not predict any-

thing. It becomes simply a verbal formula which the graduate
student repeats and believes because the professor has said it so
often. This is not science, but faith; not theory, but theology.
Whether it is hand-waving or number-waving or equation-
waving, a theory is not a theory unless it can be disproved. That
is, unless it can be falsified by some possible experimental
outcome.

In chemistry, the resonance theorists will, of course, suppose
that I am criticizing *them;* while the molecular-orbital theorists
will suppose I am criticizing *them.* But their actions—our actions,
for I include myself among them—speak for themselves. A failure
to agree for 30 years is public advertisement of a failure to
disprove.

My purpose here, however, is not to call names, but rather to
say that we are all sinners, and that in every field and in every
laboratory we need to try to formulate multiple alternative
hypotheses sharply enough to be capable of disproof.

SYSTEMATIC APPLICATION

I think the work methods of a number of scientists have been
testimony to the power of strong inference. Is success not due
in many cases to systematic use of Bacon's "surest rules and
demonstrations" as much as to rare and unattainable intellectual
power? Faraday's famous *Diary*,[16] or Fermi's *Notebooks*[3,17]
show how they believed in the effectiveness of daily steps in
applying formal inductive methods to one problem after another.

Within eight weeks after the discovery of X-rays, Roentgen had
identified 17 of their major properties. Every student should
read his first paper.[18] Each demonstration in it is a little jewel of
inductive inference. How else could the proofs have gone so
fast, except by a method of maximum effectiveness?

Organic chemistry has been the spiritual home of strong inference from the beginning. Do the bonds alternate in benzene
or are they equivalent? If the first, there should be five di-sub-
stituted derivatives; if the second, three. And three it is.[19] This
is a strong-inference test; not a matter of measurement, of
whether there are grams or milligrams of the products, but a
matter of logical alternatives. How else could the tetrahedral

carbon atom or the hexagonal symmetry of benzene have been inferred, 50 years before they could be confirmed by X-ray and infrared measurement?

We realize that it was out of this kind of atmosphere that Pasteur came to the field of biology. Can anyone doubt that he brought with him a completely different method of reasoning? Every two or three years he moved, to one biological problem after another, from optical activity to the fermentation of beet sugar, to the "diseases" of wine and beer, to the disease of silkworms, to the problem of "spontaneous generation," to the anthrax disease of sheep, to rabies. In each of these fields, there were experts in Europe who knew a hundred times as much as Pasteur; yet each time he solved problems in a few months that they had not been able to solve. Obviously it was not encyclopedic knowledge that produced his success; and obviously it was not simply luck when it was repeated over and over again; it can only have been the systematic power of a special method of exploration. Are bacteria falling in? Make the necks of the flasks S-shaped. Are they sucked in by the partial vacuum? Put in a cotton plug. Week after week, his crucial experiments built up the logical tree of exclusions. The drama of strong inference in molecular biology today is only a repetition of Pasteur's story.

The grand scientific syntheses, like those of Newton or Maxwell, are rare and individual achievements that stand outside any rule or method. Nevertheless it is interesting to note that several of the great synthesizers have also shown the strong-inference habit of thought in their other work, as Newton did in the inductive proofs of his *Opticks,* and Maxwell in his experimental proof that three and only three colors are needed in color visions.

A YARDSTICK OF EFFECTIVENESS

I think the evident effectiveness of the systematic use of strong inference suddenly gives us a yardstick for thinking about the effectiveness of scientific methods in general. Surveys. Taxonomy. Design of equipment. Systematic measurements and tables. Theoretical computations. All have their proper and honored place, provided they are parts of a chain of precise induction of how nature works. Unfortunately, all too often they become ends in themselves, mere time-serving from the point of view of real scientific advance, a hypertrophied methodology that justifies itself into a lore of respectability.

Some scientists may feel a little resentment against this kind of discussion, supposing that I am attacking all survey work, all taxonomy, and so on. I think any person who feels this way should ask himself if he is not being defensive, perhaps because he feels some qualms he has hidden from himself about how the value of his own use of his abilities would stand up under self-examination. We are creatures of habit and comfort and often do not want to have to think too hard about possibly changing our methods. I do not attack any method; I only say, think explicitly about what the alternatives are, and what their relative penetration and effectiveness might be. The exploration of a new field of science is somewhat like the exploration of an unknown continent. At first, certainly, you must come ashore wide-eyed, looking at everything, because you do not know what to expect; this is the survey period. Later, you see regularities and parallels to the birds and beasts and geology you have known before, and you make lists and classify them; this is taxonomy and the necessary operational definition of phenomena. But sooner or later, you must begin to ask analytical yes–no questions: Does the source of this river lie on this side of the mountains or the other? Alternative hypotheses: strong inference, when the crucial experiment is made. But my point is that this stage of analytical reasoning is often delayed far too long by men who let their "survey" degenerate into random dabbling and their "taxonomy" degenerate into routine collection.

We praise the "lifetime of study," but in dozens of cases in every field, what was needed was not a lifetime but rather a few short months or weeks of analytical inductive inference. We need initial surveys, but in any new area, we should try, like Roentgen, to see how fast we can pass from the general survey to analytical inferences. We need broad knowledge, but we should always try, like Pasteur, to see whether we can reach strong inferences that encyclopedism could not discern.

We speak piously of taking measurements and doing small studies that will "add another brick to the temple of science."

Most such bricks just lie around the brickyard.[20] Tables of constants have their place and value, but the study of one spectrum after another, if not frequently reevaluated, may become a substitute for thinking, a sad waste of intelligence in a research lab, and a mistraining whose crippling effects may last a lifetime.

To paraphrase an old saying: Beware of the man of one method or one instrument, either experimental or theoretical. He tends to become method-oriented rather than problem-oriented. The method-oriented man is shackled; the problem-oriented man is at least reaching freely toward what is most important. Strong inference redirects a man to problem-orientation, but it requires him to be willing repeatedly to put aside his last methods and teach himself new ones.

In the opposite direction, I think that anyone who asks the question of scientific effectiveness will also conclude that much of the mathematicizing in physics and chemistry today is irrelevant if not misleading.

The great value of mathematical formulation is that when an experiment agrees with a calculation to five decimal places, a great many alternative hypotheses are pretty well excluded. (Though the Bohr theory and the Schrödinger theory both predict exactly the same Rydberg constant!) But when the fit is only to two decimal places, or one, it may be a trap for the unwary; it may be no better than any rule-of-thumb extrapolation, and some other kind of qualitative exclusion might be more rigorous for testing the assumptions and more important to scientific understanding than the quantitative fit.

I know that this is like saying that the emperor has no clothes. Today we preach that science is not science unless it is quantitative. We substitute correlations for causal studies, and physical equations for organic reasoning. Measurements and equations are supposed to sharpen thinking; but in my observation they more often tend to make the thinking non-causal and fuzzy. They tend to become the object of scientific manipulation instead of auxiliary tests of crucial inferences.

Many, perhaps most, of the great issues of science are qualitative, not quantitative, even in physics and chemistry. Equations and measurements are useful when and only when they are related to proof; but proof or disproof comes first, and is, in fact, strongest when it is absolutely convincing without any quantitative measurement.

Or to say it another way, you can catch phenomena in a logical box or in a mathematical box. The logical box is coarse but strong. The mathematical box is finegrained but flimsy. The mathematical box is a beautiful way of wrapping up a problem, but it will not hold the phenomena unless they have been caught in a logical box to begin with.

What I am saying is that in numerous areas that we call science, we have come to like our habitual ways, and our studies that can be continued indefinitely. We measure, we define, we compute, we analyze; but we do not exclude. And this is not the way to use our minds most effectively or to make the fastest progress in solving scientific questions.

Of course it is easy—and all too common—for one scientist to call the others unscientific. My point is not that my particular conclusions here are necessarily correct, but that we have long needed some absolute standard of possible scientific effectiveness by which to measure how well we are succeeding in various areas—a standard that many could agree on and that would be undistorted by the scientific pressures and fashions of the times and the vested interests and busywork that they develop. It is not public evaluation I am interested in so much as a private measure by which to compare one's own scientific performance with what it might be. I believe that strong inference provides this kind of standard of what the maximum possible scientific effectiveness could be—as well as a recipe for reaching it.

AIDS TO STRONG INFERENCE

How can we learn the method and teach it? It is not difficult.

The most important thing is to keep in mind that this kind of thinking is not a lucky knack but a system that *can* be taught and learned. The molecular biologists today are living proof of it. The second thing is to be explicit and formal and regular about it, to spend a half hour or an hour of analytical time each day writing out the logical tree and the alternatives and crucial experiments explicitly in a permanent notebook. I have discussed elsewhere the value of Fermi's notebook method, the effect it had on his colleagues and students, and the testimony that it "can be adopted by anyone with profit." [3]

It is true that it takes great courtesy to teach the method, especially to one's peers—or their students. The strong-inference point of view is so resolutely critical of methods of work and values in science that any attempt to compare specific cases is likely to sound both smug and destructive. Mainly one should try to teach it by example and by exhorting to self-analysis and self-improvement only in general terms, as I am doing here.

But I will mention one severe but useful private test—a touchstone of strong inference—that removes the necessity for third-person criticism, because it is a test that anyone can learn to carry with him for use as needed. It is our old friend the Baconian "exclusion," but I call it "The Question." Obviously it should be applied to one's own thinking as much as or more than to others'. It consists of asking in your own mind, on hearing any scientific explanation or theory put forward:

"But sir, what experiment could *dis*prove your hypothesis?"

Or on hearing a scientific experiment described:

"But sir, what hypothesis does your experiment *dis*prove?"

This goes straight to the heart of the matter. It forces everyone to refocus on the central question of whether there is a testable scientific step forward or not.

If such a question were asked aloud, many a supposedly great scientist would sputter and turn livid and would want to throw the questioner out, as a hostile witness! Such a man is less than he appears, for he is obviously not accustomed to think in terms of alternative hypotheses and crucial experiments for himself; and one might also wonder about the state of science in the field he is in. But who knows, the question might educate him, and the field too!

On the other hand, I think that throughout most of molecular biology and nuclear physics, the response to The Question would be to outline immediately not one, but several tests to disprove the hypothesis!—and it would turn out that the speaker already had two or three graduate students working on them!

I almost think that government agencies could make use of

this kind of touchstone. It is not true that all science is equal, or that we cannot justly compare the effectiveness of scientists by any method except by a mutual-recommendation system. The man to watch, the man to put your money on, is not the man who wants "to make a survey" or a "more detailed study," but the man with the notebook, the man with the alternative hypotheses and the crucial experiments; the man who knows how to answer your question of disproof, and is already working on it.

There are some really hard problems, some high-information problems, ahead of us in several fields, problems of photosynthesis, of cellular organization, of the molecular structure and organization of the nervous system, not to mention some of our social and international problems. It seems to me that the fastest method of progress in such complex areas, the most effective way of using our brains, is going to be to set down explicitly at each step just what the question is, and what all the alternatives are, and then to set up crucial experiments to try to disprove some. Problems of this complexity, if they can be solved at all, can be solved only by men generating and excluding possibilities with maximum effectiveness, to obtain high information per unit time: men willing to work a little bit at thinking.

When whole groups of scientists begin to concentrate like that, I believe we may see the molecular-biology phenomenon repeated over and over again, with order-of-magnitude increases in the rate of scientific understanding in almost every field.

Channels of Change

Every revolution was first a thought in one man's mind. . . .
Every reform was once a private opinion.

—Emerson

Social Chain-Reactions

If we did not threaten and challenge each other, we could easily make the world a safe and pleasant place to live in. This seems so obvious, so simple, and so intelligent! And yet it is not easy to see how intelligence can get us from here to there. Men of good sense and even of goodwill differ violently on what the path should be, and on what the first step should be, and on whether any particular first step will be more dangerous or less dangerous than the situation we are now in. You and I, of course, may agree most intelligently on what may be the wisest course. But our personal powers appear to be so feeble!—And it is not clear just how we two could persuade or coerce the whole mixed-up world, or even our own country, to see this clear light of ours and to follow it.

It seems to me that this is a central problem for the human race and will continue to be one for a long time to come. Among conflicting counsels of good sense, what is the best sense? And how can we translate the best sense into common sense, and into common sensible actions coordinated to some degree, even across group boundaries and national boundaries? We need to find out how to anticipate consequences more accurately and how to amplify the delicate and uncertain powers of our highest intelligence into directed and effective acts that will reduce our collective tensions and meet our collective needs.

The important and hopeful thing I want to emphasize in the next few chapters is that this kind of amplification of intelligence is not impossible. Business and military organizations are already using methods such as "operations analysis" and "game theory" to multiply the effectiveness of intelligence in organizational situations and in conflict situations. These are problems with a limited frame of reference. But I would like to suggest here that if we analyze social chains and social causation, we may be able to discover or invent even more powerful methods that will help us deal with some of the larger and hitherto more intractable problems of our society.

The key word in what I will have to say is the word *amplification*. I believe that this concept has not been sufficiently emphasized in thinking about how intelligence can make itself effective. We see its importance as soon as we consider how, in the biological world, the brain directs the activities of an animal or a person. The brain is a rather small organ. Yet it receives information from the senses and makes decisions that are amplified and carried through the metabolizing pathways of the nerves until they are amplified again in the muscles and serve to trigger the full physical powers of the body into achieving what the brain decides is needed.

Likewise for a nation. The decision-making group in a nation is frequently a rather small group, whether it stands at the top of the official pyramid or works indirectly behind the scenes. Yet such a group can often channel the entire economic and military power of the country into one direction, sometimes with and sometimes without the full consent of the individuals involved.

In a democracy, even outside official channels, there are opportunities for small groups to be suprisingly effective. A group that wishes to reform society—to achieve woman suffrage or to ban the bomb—frequently starts with a very few people, sometimes only one. Thinking they see a better way of doing things, they are sometimes able to enlist and guide the additional forces of other men in a tremendous self-amplifying process until the result is achieved. It is obviously important for any reform group to have some idea of when and how they can hope to initiate a self-amplifying process and when they cannot.

REFORM BY SOCIAL CHAIN-REACTION

In fact, I believe that the mere restatement of the reform problem in terms of self-amplification puts it in a new light. For by amplification, I mean what can be called technically "a social chain-reaction with positive feedback." Many of the processes in society can be thought of as multiple interconnected chain reactions. Biochemists have long taken this view in describing processes in a biological organism. Occasionally one sees the notion of a chain-reaction applied to such social processes as the growth of science or technology, but sociologists and political scientists seem not to have emphasized the concept very much so far.

Certainly they seem not to have worked out the full implications of the analogy, with its rich and suggestive auxiliary concepts such as "critical size," "multiplication factors," "stability and instability"—depending on "negative or positive feedback"—"exponential decay" and "exponential growth," and the important concept of manipulation and control by "control rods." Monetary theory does make use of a number of these concepts, including the concept of control, and a few of the concepts are also used casually sometimes in describing the exponential growth of population or the growth of belligerence between powerful states up to the point of a runaway explosion. I believe the chain-reaction analogy, including the control problem, needs to be explored much more thoroughly in these cases. I also believe that it can be applied profitably to less spectacular social phenomena such as the growth and decline of whole cultures, or the formation of schools of art, or to social reform and social change in general.

We will see that the chain-reaction point of view gives us an especially clear understanding of the relation between the role of the individual and the role of determinism in history. A stabilized chain-reaction system, such as the economic system or even the subsystem associated with a federal bureau, has, within its limits of stability, a certain "unstoppable" character, a certain inevitability about its operations. There is an inevitability of a different kind in the explosion or the decay of an unstable chain reaction. We see this in such social instances as the decline of kings or the rise of the industrial revolution, in a runaway inflation or in the growth of belligerence between competing powers, or in the sudden simultaneous appearance of similar inventions in many different laboratories. All these phenomena, stable and unstable, have a deterministic appearance because there seems to be little that anyone or any group can do directly to speed them up or slow them down, once they have passed some critical point of stability or instability.

On the other hand, it is equally clear that under certain conditions, the slightest of causes—an accident to a dictator, or a new invention, or a cogent idea—can be amplified by social chain-reactions until it changes the whole structure of the world. Gandhi stands and India is liberated. Hahn and Strassmann find fission in a few atoms of uranium, and the international political scene turns upside down. This is what makes the small amount of money spent on research such a powerful force.

In the light of such possibilities, the future becomes quite indeterminate and unpredictable, except to men with the insight to anticipate such results. The least fluctuation, perceptible only to a single man—a leak in the brakes or a dream of Pan-Germany—may be amplified into effects as large as the maximum energy output that the species can control. Society is probably capable of many alternative amplifications at a given time. It may often happen that the one that "wins" is decided by the amplified efforts of a single person. The individual act of the individual man then comes to be of supreme importance; and the discoverer or seer, the one who can point out a path that great numbers can follow with personal satisfaction, holds history in his hands.

To make such an analysis more precise, we will need to emphasize the distinction we have already made between two different kinds of chain-reaction situations. One of these is like the controlled atomic pile. The other is like a subcritical or supercritical atomic bomb. The first is represented in society by *self-stabilizing* organizations and self-stabilizing situations. These are characterized by internal or external "negative feedback"; that is, by a return to their previous equilibrium when disturbed.

The second category is represented by *self-amplifying* or *self-destroying* organizations or situations. These are characterized by "positive feedback," so that they run away from equilibrium either in one direction to the point of indefinite growth or in the other direction to the point of vanishing. It is this second category that offers the most obvious possibilities for the amplification of intelligence, although we will mention some of the things that can be done to change self-stabilizing situations.

SEED OPERATIONS

The most straightforward of the amplification possibilities is what I would like to call a "seed operation"—a ten-cent phone call that produces a billion dollars' worth of results. A new technical invention, such as the dynamo, or the telephone, or the airplane, frequently has this self-amplifying character. But there are many kinds of social seed operations, too. A number of individuals in history have demonstrated that they could bring off such coups again and again. We need to examine in detail some of the achievements of Leo Szilard, for example, who played a conscious seed role not only as a scientist in radio-chemistry and biology but also as a scientist-politician. He helped initiate the Einstein letter to Roosevelt that started the atomic bomb project; and later the Franck report, which urged that the bomb be demonstrated before it was used in war. He played an important seed role toward the end of his life in his population control and disarmament studies, and in his invention of new methods of political action.

We see the importance of individual intelligence and initiative in such matters when we compare the American atomic bomb project with that of the Germans, who started out ahead of the British and Americans but who never got off the ground, fortunately for the rest of us, because they had no Szilard or Wigner to trigger them into a project of sufficient boldness.

Bernard Baruch and Vannevar Bush are others in our own time who have tried to pull off a series of social seed operations. But such attempts are not new in history. Benjamin Franklin is closely comparable to Szilard in his conscious and successful efforts to initiate seed projects for the advancement of science and the improvement of society. He founded a press, a magazine, a debating society, a philosophical society, a library, and several other valuable services. And by his reorganization of the postal service for the fast delivery of newspapers, he increased at one stroke the number of informed and critical citizens ripe for independence.

Lobbyists and revolutionists, of course, have always known to aim for the jugular, that is, for the "foci of power" in the administrative apparatus, where their efforts can be amplified by the normal operations of the apparatus itself. But I am interested here especially in what can be done by dedicated persons outside the apparatus when they use their ingenuity to invent self-amplifying social ideas. A magnificent example was the creation of a stable Constitution and government out of a chaotic situation by a small group of Federalists. Theirs was a conscious seed operation, with long-range effects that were foreseen and planned for remarkably well. Standard time was adopted mainly because of the efforts of one man, Charles Dowd. And pay-as-you-go income tax, which has undoubtedly greatly multiplied the resources of the government in our time, was the single-handed invention of Beardsley Ruml. The sponsorship of research on oral contraceptives after World War II was a social seed operation that may yet pay off.

More conventional examples of amplification are found in the "multiplier projects" of the Point Four Program of U.S. foreign aid in the 1950's. These were projects which were designed to be demonstrations that would be imitated extensively as soon as their success was seen. Evidently, seed operations are possible whenever great intellectual or social energies are available and ripe for change.

SOCIO-TECHNICAL INVENTIONS

A second type of self-amplifying possibility that should be important to the reformer, as well as to the administrator, is the chain of behavior associated with a technical invention, or with what I would like to call a socio-technical invention. The alteration of group behavior in such chain reactions can be so dramatic and extensive that one is almost tempted to think that every social problem might be solvable by one of those socio-technical inventions, especially if it is endowed with a pleasurable feedback character, and so with a self-amplifying character at every step for the individual user.

The kind of thing I have in mind is the elimination of barter and the creation of commerce by the invention of the coin. The principle involved is simple—even a chimpanzee can be taught to use a kind of money—but it had to wait thousands of years for the inventor. Or take the horse collar: According to one theory, this technical invention—this multiplier project—was what · enlarged the medieval farms and created a surplus of production, and so made possible the Renaissance.

Evidently if you want to create one world, you should start with a wind-tunnel and invent the airplane. If you want to reduce population, you must devise a personal payback, a personal incentive, and not a clumsy medical device. To educate billions rapidly, invent programmed teaching by books or machines with instant individual feedback. To feed the world on algae—that "nasty little green vegetable"—turn it into a cocktail snack; that is, find a way to make it delicious and desirable.

I group these examples together because they have one thing in common. Each depends on a socio-technical device that makes every individual step in the social process a desirable step, and hence inevitable. This is what makes the chain of amplification possible, and inevitable. Social energy tends to run along channels of personal satisfaction; downhill, so to speak. The cause and the direction of progress are explained by the rule that "Nature gives a prize to every single step in it," as Bagehot said. In order to carry out any great project, the future good of the group must be anticipated and turned into present and individual good, into a reward for every step that is taken in the right direction.

To get a new factory or a new highway, money must be borrowed, interest paid, workers paid, before the anticipated goods or benefits come forth. The coin of payment is a symbolic subdivision of the anticipated good, but with a tangible and current buying power. How vast and yet how easy such projects can be, compared to the grudging inefficiency of collective or coerced construction, where the individual has little but the hope of a later reward, and the project must therefore be dragged

over a hill of reluctance and inattention by a dwindling thread
of enthusiasm! The faith that moves social mountains is a self-
catalytic chain-reacting faith in present personal advantage.

FEEDBACK TOKENS

I think we will see that, if we put our minds to it, we can
invent new tokens, like the coin, that would serve in other areas
to translate long-range group needs into current individual acquiescence or effort. In World War II, for example, rationing
coupons were used with remarkable success by the Office of Price
Administration in a coupon flowback system that induced com-
pliance with the rationing law through all the stages from pro-
ducer to consumer. In quite another direction, we can see the
potential power of individual feedback rewards by considering
what would happen if we had sexually selective contraceptives
that would give us only boy babies or girl babies as desired. With
such an invention, many of the individual resistances to contraceptives would go down in an instant, regardless of price. In a
generation we would have a world sexually unbalanced in just
the ratio the parents wanted, most probably with the number and
total fertility of women greatly reduced and with their status
greatly enhanced.

In still another direction, in the handling of mob violence,
think of the increased acquiescence we could get if we invented
tranquillizing gases for control, so as to reduce individual antagonism, instead of using tear gas, vomitories, and bullets, which
only intensify it.

Undoubtedly it takes a moment of inspiration in an uncon-
ventional mind to devise our great and simple socio-technical
inventions—the coin, the key, the postage stamp, the alphabet, the
contraceptive, the credit card. The inventor, if he is to have any
control over the direction in which his seed will grow, must
understand thoroughly the process and the feedbacks that he is
trying to change. (It took insight to see that credit cards would
promote travel and entertainment so much better than ordinary
checks and money.) But when such inventions appear, they blow
away the old habits and attitudes and organizations like dust.
The laborious frontal attacks of uplift groups and mass meetings

and legislation—laborious because they are attacks at the stabilizing level on self-stabilizing systems—become unnecessary. Perhaps organizations and groups should offer rewards to stimulate sociotechnical inventions that could lead in desired directions. To use a biochemical analogy, such tokens would be like "enzymes" that would take us to our goals by a series of roundabout and easy steps instead of over a psychic and organizational "activation barrier." It may be that we have not even scratched the surface of what can be done to manipulate and coordinate our social efforts easily into mutually satisfying channels by the use of feedback tokens and other individual-reward devices.

There is another important chain-reaction possibility that should also be thought about, although it will be too complex to explore here in detail. It is the possibility of using one social amplification process to head off another, undesirable, amplification process. This is one of the important principles in biological control. We can prevent rabies, after the infection has set in, by injecting a vaccine that will evoke rapidly multiplying antibodies. The reproductive chain-reaction of the damaging screwworm fly can be quenched by the introduction of sterile males, so that the fly is completely eradicated over vast areas, in exact accordance with the predictions of population theory. The social analogy of using chains to stop chains deserves careful study, for this method does not require such elaborate anticipation as the design of anticipatory feedbacks does, and it could be a powerful last-ditch method of control.

CONTRAST WITH DESCRIPTIVE SOCIOLOGY

Let me digress for a moment to emphasize that this chain-reaction and socio-technical approach to be examined here, with its emphasis on causal sequences and on operational understanding, seems to me in striking contrast to the attempts by some sociologists to discuss the interaction of technology with modern society. I have in mind one recent book by several well-known and distinguished sociology professors which pretends to be a text on this subject, but which is hardly more than a bulky collection of clichés about how things are getting bigger and more troublesome. Even allowing for differences in the viewpoint of men in different disciplines, it seems to me that this descriptive approach does not really demonstrate the first thing about how technology acts or interacts with society. These men devote several chapters to the pleased discovery that elaborate geometrically increasing or exponential curves (of the kind that are, of course, characteristic of an amplifying chain-reaction) predict some technological growth rates better than linear curves. But there is no understanding of the crucial chain-process that creates the exponential, so there is no discussion of where the exponential behavior will stop, or the possible relation to population exponentials; or why some technological advances are adopted and grow while others are ignored; or how we can know beforehand which variables will turn out to be increasing or decreasing exponentials and which will be linear curves, oscillating curves, step functions, exhaustion-of-resources curves, and so on. I do not pretend that all these answers are easy to obtain for different kinds of technological advance and socio-technical invention; but these are the crucial questions to ask and to try to understand so that some degree of prediction will be possible.

In this particular book, the social scientists are impressed by numbers. They repeatedly quote big-sounding statistics which turn out to be trivial, and their tables are filled with numbers supposedly having seven "significant figures." They give us technological profundities that defy parody; for example, "Whenever a result occurs, something has varied. . . . Thus when a telephone is first created, there is a variation from nothing, that is, no telephone, to a telephone." And on atomic problems, they proclaim: "Our earlier analysis of the atomic crisis indicates that what we are confronted with is a specific example of that general type of problem which may be described as a menacing cultural lag involving exploitation and aggression." ! ! !

The social scientists like categories, and categories crossed with categories to make pigeon-holes. They say, "Culture Has Three Dimensions . . . a vast five-layer cake, stretching back infinitely into the past, and sliced from front to back in six institutional slices." On another subject, they speak of "a process which is a combination of the two subprocesses of *dispersal* and *convergence*." (Italics theirs.) A good set of categories can evidently straddle anything.

This so-called social science is journalistic where it should be thorough, cliquish where it should be detached, pretentious where it should have ideas, and clabber-mouthed where it should be clear. Its medieval categories do not give us any new understanding of anything or tell us how to do anything. It is quite innocent of the principles of technological social change and social chain reactions that are already being put into large practice by a number of thoughtful men and organizations today.

And the last section of this book is called "The Coming Upsurge of Social Science"!

My remarks about this particularly fruity example are not aimed against all sociology. It is vain to set one field against another or one useful approach against another. There is much sociology that has told us a great deal about how our society works and how we can change it. But there is a difference in every field between minds that analyze causal relations, quantitatively or not, and minds that turn out categorical mishmash or attempt to impress us with statistics and equations. Karl Pearson made a brilliant and valuable contribution in attempting to make qualitative relationships numerical, but many of his followers and their students in the social fields have let a blind worship of decimal measurements and correlations sidetrack any thinking about causes and mechanisms and functional relations.

It is time for more men who are willing to discuss *how* things happen in society—whether they are natural scientists, social scientists, lawyers, politicians, or humanists—to think seriously and analytically about whether we are collectively going where we want to go, and if not, what detailed operational steps we can take to change it. After the sociologists have given us such a magnificent demonstration, I think none of us need be ashamed of any nonprofessional observations or uncertain proposals we bring to the discussion.

SELF-STABILIZING TENSION SYSTEMS

Returning to our general discussion of chain-reactions, I want to touch on the final central question that will concern all of us, the question as to whether any of the methods of amplification we have mentioned could be applied to control more intelligently our chain-reacting and self-stabilizing international tensions today. (The belligerence is self-amplifying, but the tensions are self-stabilizing; the one produces the danger, the other the difficulty.) Can any socio-technical invention or any seed operation be devised that would reduce the danger of these tensions building up to an explosion? Probably the chain-reacting race for space, and the race to aid underdeveloped countries, have helped a little, by bleeding off some of the energy into other forms of competition. But it appears to me that we may also need a new enzyme, a new coin of payment or clear advantage whose pursuit would tend to lead each individual act of the superpowers into easier channels toward the anticipated good of a less dangerous world.

There is no doubt that such a social solution may be difficult to invent. But self-stabilizing tension situations are also particularly difficult to change in our society by more conventional means. They differ from self-stabilizing organizations, which we more or less understand how to manipulate and coerce, because they have no central entity on which we can put the whole blame or the responsibility for change. To use the chain-reaction analogy, we do not know how to "push in" the control rods in a tension situation because there is no familiar organizational pyramid or control-rod structure; and we do not see the many different kinds of control rods that may nevertheless be available.

As we consider this problem, it may help us if we realize that not all such tension situations are bad or dangerous. In a country such as England or the United States which has majority elections and certain other political safeguards, there is a self-stabilizing tension that tends to maintain two political parties and centralizes them, and yet keeps them in check. (We will see later that the equalization and centralization of the parties can be understood from the game-theoretical minimax choices of leaders seeking election.) Most of us now think that this mutually-corrective tension is one of the most valuable parts of the democratic process. We will be able to see particularly well, the wisdom of the Founding Fathers in designing this and other tensions into our system, as soon as we compare this system with the unstable governments and petty factions common in countries with other constitutional devices such as proportional representation (where the game-theoretical choices lead to factionalism) .

CONVERTING INTERNATIONAL TENSIONS

This suggests the thought that we might reduce dangerous international tensions by converting them to party tensions, provided these were of the beneficial rather than the disruptive sort. For example, what would happen if United Nations representatives could be elected by districts from each country rather than be appointed by national governments? With majority elections, a two-party system would probably arise very rapidly, cutting across national lines just as the American two-party system cuts across state lines. The necessity for each bloc to enlist support for itself in other countries would then begin to mitigate the dangers of bloc voting and unilateral bloc action. And yet, each of the superpowers might be persuaded that it had much to gain from such a change in the United Nations method of representation—the one because it might gain support from minorities in other countries, the other because it would increase the democracy of the representation. A minor election proposal of this type might have great political consequences.

This illustration is oversimplified, but it serves to show that rather subtle changes in the rules, especially if their interacting chains of feedbacks were better adapted to the realities of the world, might have a good chance of success. A feedback system in which the self-centered national actions direct themselves automatically, so to speak, to good collective ends is simpler and more effective than threats, guards, and inspections. If groups could be given satisfaction methods other than threats for getting their share of the rights and privileges of the world—including the right to be free from threats—they would not need to threaten.

It obviously will be important for political theorists, legislators and devisers of world institutions to think as clearly as the Federalists did about the feedbacks in our social and political systems, so that they will understand both how to create self-stabilizing tensions in a society and how to destroy or redirect them when they become dangerous. I believe that if intelligent

scientists and men of affairs will begin to look at tension situations in this way, with stabilizing and destabilizing processes in
mind, they may be able to invent new socio-technical devices
and seed operations that will make possible the manipulation
of such situations in directions that all of us desire and will
profit from.

There is obviously an element of danger in the advocacy of
such powerful self-amplification methods as I am describing. Like
any principles of operation, they may be used for good or bad
ends. But this makes it doubly necessary for men of goodwill to
take a close and analytical look at them, to see whether the
amplification processes now going on are not leading us by design
or accident to thoroughly bad ends. I am beginning to believe
that in any social endeavor, it is the analysis of chain-reacting
social processes that will enable us to choose the best course and
will indicate the most effective ways for our intelligence to multiply its feeble energies. The future is waiting to respond to a
touch, if it is the right touch. It is ingenuity we need, not
lamentations. The world's future becomes almost plastic in the
light of these possibilities.

Science creates more science, like a fire; and the conditions for nursing it and keeping it burning are much the same.

Science as a Chain-Reaction

Men have been using fires for a long time, and everyone, even the most insulated apartment dweller, understands more or less the principles of laying a fire, lighting it and keeping it burning, and preventing it from smoking. More recently, we have achieved a second kind of controlled chain-reaction, not running on chemical energy like a fire, but on nuclear energy. This kind is so expensive and so dangerous that the charming irregularity and haphazardness of the campfire have had to be eliminated. But it has numerous technical similarities to ordinary fires that are interesting and physically quite exact.

It is amusing and, I believe, instructive, to see how exact the parallels are between these inanimate chain-reactions and many biological systems. A plant or an animal is, among other things, a complex physiological chain-reaction, and many of its chemical processes and its control and equilibrium problems can be described in chain-reaction language. A society is also a chain-reaction in several different aspects; economic, political, and intellectual.

Is it not possible to use these analogies in an explicit way to illuminate biological and social and intellectual phenomena? I think it is. I think it is startling to see how many useful insights into some of our complex social processes are suggested by taking seriously the analogy to a familiar chain-reaction such as fire. And it is particularly striking to see how this analogy method can be applied to analyzing one particular social and intellectual chain-reaction, the reaction we call scientific research.

I should emphasize at the outset that I am not trying to make a "universal theory" here. I am not going to claim that all types of social or intellectual activity are chain-reactions. Science is a chain-like system because discoveries are not made in isolation, but in sequence, in a progressive chain of steps; they grow out of other discoveries and interact and multiply to produce new discoveries, as Derek de Solla Price has emphasized in *Little Science, Big Science* and other writings. We see this demonstrated almost quantitatively in certain fields, for example in the 100,000-fold increase in the energy of particle-accelerators in physics in the last 35 years. Our ability to design such an exponential improvement in our machines, with the energy multiplied 10-fold in every successive seven-year period—a feature that Enrico Fermi often remarked on—is almost conclusive evidence of an accelerating intellectual chain-reaction of some kind. What we call **Progress** is often equivalent to the statement that exponential chain-reactions of this sort are still going on—that our intellectual "multiplication factor" k for successive achievements is still greater than 1.00.

But there are other fields, for example, art and music and belles-lettres, which, although they have chain elements such as imitation and the formation of schools and societies, are not represented by chain-reactions or by exponential growth in their important central achievements. The element of invention in the arts is a random personal element, not a cumulative one. The Western artist today is not necessarily better than the Renaissance artist or the classical Greek. In such fields there is no Progress, there is only Uniqueness. This is not to belittle such activities; it is only to say that they are not accelerating chain-reactions, and that for them the multiplication factor k cannot be defined. I think it is this non-expanding characteristic that is mainly responsible for our recent neglect of the academic humanities compared to the more technical subjects whose chain-reacting character has been continually amplifying their vital role in our daily lives.

GENERAL PROPERTIES COMMON
TO CHAIN-REACTIONS

Let us begin our consideration of the analogies by examining some of the general properties of chain-reactions, their purposes, their structural form and organization, and the similarities in their variables.

The curious thing about the purposes of a chain-reaction is the multiplicity of them, in almost every case. This has not caused the surprise it deserves, that a chain system can be turned in so many different directions. A chain-reaction is a kind of flowing totality, with many aspects, and we emphasize one or another of these according to what we want. In using the chemical chain-reaction of fire, for example, our purposes are now so numerous that it is amusing to make a catalog of them just to see how many there are. We may use its heat in a furnace, its light in a candle, its noise in a firecracker, its destructiveness to burn garbage or to blow up enemies, or the direct pressure of the reaction-system to run a gasoline engine. We may use it to "breed" a richer fuel (in the nuclear language), as in coke ovens. The farm wife may use the ashes, its "fission products," so to speak, to make soap, and its smoke to repel mosquitoes. Or we may want the exhaust gases, as in a coal gasification process or in a fire balloon. Each of these properties and products requires a different type of reaction vessel for most efficient extraction. A history of mankind might well be written around the developing historical series of reaction vessels of each type.

The parallel with nuclear chain-reactions is clear, and anyone may be entertained by trying to see for himself how many of these purposes have a nuclear counterpart. Our social chain-reactions are multipurpose in the same way. A chicken farm may be operated primarily to produce chickens, to produce eggs, or to produce money. We might regard the social chain-reaction of commerce and industry as a device to make goods, to make money, to make work, or to make a colorful spectacle. The commercial organization—the reaction vessel—and its method of operation will be different according to which function is emphasized.

It is not simply whimsy to include the function of making a spectacle. This is a purpose of our chain-reactions which is frequently underestimated in importance. We get a kinesthetic pleasure from watching fires or from sensing the commercial bustle of a city. The spectacle of multiplication fascinates us. Chain-processes seem, and are, so much more *alive* than the rest of the universe. A waterfall. A thunderstorm. Newborn puppies. We feel their changes of form, their setbacks and advances, increases and decreases of k, as though we were part of them, as though their reaction systems were our very own. And are they not? Chain-reactions represent the side of nature which is least mechanical, where we can empathize and identify with ongoing and universal processes that we, too, represent.

One special reason for our empathy is that steady-state chain-reactions develop a structural form and organization far beyond what seems to be demanded by the reaction-equations. There is form and organization, both spatial and temporal, in every release of energy. Even the sun has a detailed structure not obvious to the naked eye, from the nuclear-reacting core to the outer photosphere and chromosphere where the gases boil up in endless variations on their constant themes, flocculi, sunspots, prominences, flares, and solar corona, each with its characteristic structure and time dependence.

There is structure likewise in the flame of a match, with the fresh fuel on one side, the red glow in the center, the dead char behind. The air comes in from below, mixes with the chemical vapors near the wood, forms a blue ignition shell around that, and moves up into the white flame whose boundary is the envelope of a multitude of glowing particles that burn as they rise and are finally transformed into the invisible column of hot gas above.

This structural form in a chain-reaction is not merely accidental. Much of it is necessary to keep the reaction proceeding. The form becomes organic and functional form. A match would not burn in a space ship, as science-fiction is fond of pointing out. For where there is no gravity to separate the parts of the flame, they cannot perform their functions. The hot gases do not rise up, for there is no "up"; and they accumulate in a choking sphere empty of oxygen, which puts out the fire. (Undoubtedly there are analogies here to some of our social chain-reactions.) It is interesting to speculate on what different fire tools might have evolved in the absence of gravity.

VARIABLES AND SIMILARITIES

The main technical principles of chain-reactions, as seen for example in nuclear reactors, are hardly everyday knowledge, but there are numerous, fairly accurate, general accounts of what the important factors are: How at every step each neutron must produce more neutrons, with an average multiplication factor, k, greater than 1.00; how some of the neutrons fly out and get lost from the reaction, reducing k; how some minimum critical size is necessary to keep these losses from being prohibitive, making the total k less than 1.00; how the thing blows up, in geometric progression or "exponentially," if the total k is greater than 1.00; and how "control rods" can be pushed in (or pulled out) to absorb more (or less) neutrons and keep k constant, under control, at a reduced (or increased) level of the reaction; and so on.

We know all these principles, really, from our experience with fire. The fire multiplies itself—its chemical reactions are multiplied—when the flame "catches"; heat is lost from the surface; the minimum critical size is seen when we have to have a big blaze in order to get wet wood or coal started or to keep them burning; the fire "blows up," exponentially, when there is an indefinite supply of dry wood nearby, as when a house or a forest catches fire; and the external "control rods" are represented by a bellows to make the fire hotter or a spray of water to cool it off or put it out, or by a damper, which controls it in a different way. There is some stabilization or control mechanism, introduced either naturally or by design, in every steady-state chain-reaction, whether we are dealing with a stabilized low level of reaction as in a match flame or with a high level as in a furnace.

We discover the same variables, and principles, in all chain-reactions. Certain major properties of either a living organism or a fire could be written down in identical equations relating such things as fuel consumption, rate of growth or decay, lifetimes, structure, and size.

Do we not recognize this in our language? We speak of a "living flame," but this is not merely a poetic trope, it is a strict physical analogy. We take many figures of speech from the systems we know most intimately, the fire system and the life system, and apply them to each other and to other chain-reactions because the important variables behave in the same way. Live coals. Dying embers. Nursing the flame. Interest flared up. The town was dead. The factual content of a great part of lyric poetry is simply the statement of these equivalences.

We see, for example, that every chain-reacting system has its fuel or reactants. There may be one main reacting component as in a nuclear reactor, or two as in a fire or in sexual reproduction, or many, as in commerce and science. Our social reactions use a peculiar periodic fuel whose lumps need sleep and vacations to eliminate their reaction products and restore their vigor.

There are problems of contact of these components and of supply. Of impurities which dilute or absorb unwanted "side reactions." For example, in the social and intellectual fields, these are the problems of business "contacts" and intellectual contact. Of getting the bright boys into graduate school. Of throwing out the clinkers—the cranks or the inefficient.

In all chain systems, there are end products, and the problems of removing them, either for use or to keep them from diluting and smothering the reaction. The ashes of a fire. Uremic poisoning in an organism. Population pressure and emigration in a nation. Publication of results in science.

The main considerations governing the multiplication factor k are also parallel in various chain-reactions. They involve such things as the concentration of the reactants, whatever they are; the "mean free path" or time between successive reaction-steps; the losses to unwanted "side-reactions" or through the "surface"; the "minimum critical size" necessary to overcome the losses; and "delayed reactions" which determine how fast the chain-reaction will blow up or die down and how fast the control rods must work.

In social chain-reactions, what corresponds to a "surface" is the collection of points at which energy is lost or at which reactants become unavailable to the reproductive process. In human reproduction, it might be strong-minded bachelors, or the lateness of marriage. In commercial or intellectual chain-reactions, it might be red tape, or the time spent by technical brains in administrative housekeeping or in fending off inquiries.

It is losses of this kind that lead to a minimum critical size in universities and in commerce. Small units cannot compete as well. "It takes money to make money" is a popular discovery of critical size. In biology, on the other hand, small units can compete, because the critical sizes are very small, requiring just one or two "reacting" individuals in asexual or sexual reproduction, the minimum possible number.

The stoppage of reactions occurs when some external interruption or some deleterious change has taken place which reduces k too fast or too much below 1.00 to be compensated for by the available control rods. Scattering a fire; or blocking the damper. Exhaustion of fuel. Poisoning and smothering, for example, by ashes. In the economic chain-reaction, depressions. In intellectual life, the Dark Ages. In biology, the passing of the dinosaurs.

These parallels between the variables and their relationships in the different types of chain systems are sufficiently close that I believe similar mathematical equations might be written for all of them. Some of the constants might be unknown, especially in abstract systems like intellectual chain-reactions, but perhaps might be determined, as unknown constants are sometimes determined in nuclear physics, by experimenting directly with variations in the chain-reaction itself.

In what follows, I would therefore like to show how these parallels can be used as an analogy method for a nonmathematical but close analysis of scientific research as a chain-reacting system. The results will be given in the form of observations and inferences, the inferences being derived from the observations directly or indirectly by making use of fire-building as the chain-reacting prototype and parallel. That is, I believe we can learn a great deal by thinking of science quite literally as an intellectual fire. My observations have been taken from science and science departments in American universities, but I believe they are still valid qualitatively, if not quantitatively, under the somewhat different conditions in governmental and industrial scientific laboratories and in the laboratories of other countries.

MINIMUM CRITICAL SIZE IN SCIENTIFIC RESEARCH

Observation. The minimum critical size for a natural science department which includes several specialties appears to be around 15 to 20 full-time staff members.

This is approximately the minimum size of the departments at the top dozen or so American universities where most of the work in mathematics, astronomy, physics, and chemistry is produced. The best men rarely want to go to a smaller group, because of the lack of stimulation and services. Although in each of these subjects, these dozen departments together have less than half the total science faculty of the country, they have an overwhelming majority of the university research facilities, of contracts and money, and of distinguished men of science. They publish most of the research articles, edit most of the journals, and probably make over 90 per cent of the university discoveries.

A group of fifteen good men in one department can produce many times as much research as the same group in five departments of three men each at five different schools. Even separation of a department into different but adjacent buildings may case a considerable loss of research power. As for the effect of security barriers—!

The critical size for each department at each school would be much larger without the support given by the other departments and the scientific interests of the rest of the university. These act as a neutron reflector acts, or a "radiation shield" acts around a fire, in keeping up interest and reducing distractions. A small fire will catch spontaneously and keep burning longer in the close vicinity of a larger one.

It may be said by someone in a small department somewhere that this is an unfair comparison. That the big schools are good not because they are big, but because they get all the money and pay the big salaries and cut down teaching and clerical loads and so on. Partly true; but these are further indirect effects of exceeding the critical size. They are similar to buying rich fuel and giving it a forced draft to keep the reaction going. This is characteristic of an intellectual chain-reaction. The acceleration in the chain is partly produced by the fact that the hottest reactants know how to build the fire up around themselves to keep it going hotly; that is, how to persuade administrations and government officials to adopt the best reaction conditions. To a certain extent it is the chain-reaction of the fifteen men that produces these conditions as much as the conditions that produce the reaction. Cause and effect become indefinite in a chain—just as in the old chain riddle: Which came first, the chicken or the egg?

At smaller schools, many men nevertheless do research in spite of the greater difficulties. Often they can continue only because they were ignited early at one of the large centers. They can keep up the flame through reading or by occasional attendance at meetings, sharing in the general scientific glow of the nation.

Indifferent men who get into one of the big reaction centers often produce more than they would do on the outside, just as wet wood dries and begins to burn near a hot fire. Students are "fired" with enthusiasm, or turn a native brilliance to important problems that they might otherwise have neglected.

We thus reach a first important inference: Research would advance faster if the small faculties of a nation could be combined into a few large ones. A few large hot fires burn more efficiently than many small marginal ones.

It would be foolish, of course, to apply any such policy blindly. Faculties have other functions besides research (although some of these functions might also be done better in larger units). But have you ever seen one of those middle-sized American cities with two or three denominational colleges, a city college, a technical school, and a medical school, every one of these with its little two-man or three-man science departments offering a dozen courses to a few students with totally inadequate equipment? It is a waste of men and a mis-education of students. If these separated groups could combine their faculties, their funds and equipment, and their students into single departments serving the whole city and region, they could have much better equipment, with each man teaching his specialty and yet with a lighter teaching and administrative load and more time for research.

Foundations and other donors should consider giving bonus grants to get over the hurdles of tradition that block this kind of amalgamation of ineffective units. If they did, the process would take place quickly and enthusiastically, I believe, and would produce results far more important than the same money spent in direct support of research.

Rearrangements of this kind would have to be allowed some time to realize their full potentialities. Time is required to stabilize new reactor arrangements. Wet wood must be fed into a good fire slowly in order not to smother it. It is even better if new fires can be organized around centers that are already flaming, as when we reignite old embers with a torch.

This thought leads us to another inference: Research generally cannot take hold in new centers without *mass* transfer of active personnel. If we try to build a second fire from a first one by carrying over one stick at a time, it may go out before the next stick comes to join it.

The research man goes with hope to the fine position at the small school. Then he slowly becomes exhausted and discouraged by the difficulty of getting apparatus, time, appreciation, or money from the legislature. Finally, another younger enthusiast comes to join him—and this new man is now dampened more by his predecessor, this well-meaning but gloomy realist, old before his time, than he would have been by all the other difficulties.

I think the personnel policies at many institutions need to take account of this property of chain-reactions. For the long-run vigor of the fire it is important to have a periodic supply of fresh kindling; not fifteen men at once to grow discouraged together and block all new appointments for a generation; nor one man every year to grow discouraged separately; but several men together every three or four years, to keep each other vigorous and to revitalize the older men's thoughts as well.

INTELLECTUAL AIR SUPPLY

Observation.   The reactants—the scientists—must have intellectual separation as well as intellectual contact. The logs must be close enough to keep each other hot but not so close as to choke off the draft.

Separation in time and in space is needed. The individual scientist reacts best when stimulated by currents from neighboring disciplines as well as those from his own; when he is left alone to work out a thought, then brought together with others to exchange it. The fire of interactions must be stirred from time to time, but it must not be stirred constantly.

I think this looseness and partial separation is one of the reasons why universities have tended to be preferred as contractors on advanced and far-out projects. A new problem may "catch fire" from the novel approaches of a scientific group already chain-reacting on other problems, more effectively than from separate new laboratories and research bureaus set up especially to solve it. Not only do the universities have a constant supply of young "tinder" to keep the logs glowing, but they offer all kinds of random contacts for all temperaments instead of the stacked organized logs and cold channels of many non-university laboratories.

From this "principle of separation," we may make another inference: Large intimate groups devoted to single limited projects are frequently less productive than if the same personnel were more diverse in their interests or more widely separated.

The diverse university structure has tended to propagate itself for centuries. The intellectual life does not thrive on monotony or enjoy it. I think this is why the universities have generally had greater productivity of new ideas than the narrower industrial laboratories in spite of the more regular hours, larger size, and better financing of the latter.

STARTING THE SCIENTIFIC FIRE

Observation. Research success is a highly "nonlinear function" of the conditions.

What this statement means is that doubling a man's available research time can more than double his output. One man may be 30 per cent better than another on an intelligence test but a thousand times more valuable. To say it graphically, halving the distance between the logs in a fire may change its intensity by many powers of ten.

These are all consequences of the exponential dependence of a chain-reaction on k.

Inference. Research should not be directly administered by a committee. A committee has a hard time starting a fire, especially if there are any difficulties, as anyone who has ever been in such a group realizes. One man wants to blow on the flame, one to separate the twigs more, one to make them finer, one to wait for it to catch. A group rarely has the subtlety or patience to watch for the little cues that show the flame is being nursed in the right direction.

The compromise vote of a committee is a good method of making choices if the consequences are "linear functions" of the choices, that is, if a compromise between two alternatives is as good as either. If several intelligent men differ on a decision in such cases, their average judgment may be the "best" value in both the mathematical and the political sense. But with nonlinear reaction functions, the extra few per cent that the best man can give to k may be the difference between a chain-reaction working and not working.

The average of a good arrangement and a poor arrangement is probably a poor arrangement. The average of two good arrangements may be very much better, or very much worse than either.

Inference.   A good administrator is more precious than uranium, and he must be given a free hand. He develops a "feeling" for the fire, and intuitive rules of thumb and artistic touches that he cannot justify but which work for him. If you want to build a quick hot fire, don't debate it, get someone who is known to be good at it. (And give him lots of "fire-starter fluid"—which is money!)

Inference.   Research success demands the very best men.

Better three excellent men than ten good men. Better 10 good men than 10 good ones and 20 poor. A big mediocre lab dilutes the work of the best men, who must carry the rest on their backs.

Because of the nonlinearity, combined with variations from problem to problem and from lab to lab, a good man may be in a bad place and not show his talent until after he has had several tries.

Inference.   Don't meddle with a successful team.

Meddling with a good fire is apt to make it worse. Just add new fuel from time to time and stir gently.

"REACTION TIMES" IN SCIENCE

Observation. The national interaction time of ideas is of the order of a few weeks or months. This is of the order of the time that an intelligent adult can enjoy working on a difficult problem independently, without rest or further stimulation. Then he needs to communicate and interact.

This time corresponds to the delayed-reaction-time which is so important in a chain-reaction; or to the time constant for heating and cooling the reactants in a fire, which makes the difference between the quick heat of the gas fire and the slow-catching but long-burning heat of coal.

One of the main advantages of the large research group is in replacing to some extent the national interaction time by a group interaction time, which may be of the order of days or hours, permitting the much more rapid elimination of bad ideas and multiplication of good ones.

Inference. Accessible research meetings in each field should be held two or three times a year.

Inference. Research men should be sent to meetings in their own field two or three times a year. The cost of the travel is negligible compared to the increased productivity effected by the interchange. This principle is well understood in business and industry, but not always in university and government contracts; it is not the supervisor who needs his way paid to two meetings a year but his idea men.

Inference. Research people should publish several times a year. Research without publication is no research. It is no contribution to the chain-reaction process. And the man who delays much longer than this goes stale or loses his grasp of what he did earlier.

It is no accident that these frequencies of meetings and interactions agree fairly well with current American practice in the fastest-developing fields. In fact, with advanced research men now going to five or ten meetings a year, there are complaints in many areas of physics, chemistry, and biology that there are too many meetings.

Inference. The research productivity of a nation might be increased by a factor of two or more by cutting publication time and indexing time in the journals to a few weeks or less.

When publication time is longer than this, it becomes the limiting factor on the "reaction-time-constant," since meetings are only a partial method of communication. The reaction-time with present indexing practices is frequently over a year. In a crowded field, publication without indexing is no publication at all, and the publication is void until indexing is complete.

This is why physicists and biologists working today on the most advanced problems communicate principally by telephone or by face-to-face contact on their frequent trips. A casual survey indicates that most university physicists read less than one article per month in a major journal such as the *Physical Review;* it is now principally a journal of record, because any results of importance have been known among the knowing perhaps as much as eighteen months earlier. This is unfortunate because outside these "in-groups" of fifty people or so, there are many good brains in other laboratories and other countries, who might make important contributions or criticisms if they were also brought into the fast-communication channels.

Part of the trouble is obsolete printing practices which do not match those of commercial periodicals. Part of this is due to the obsolete abstracting and indexing practices, such as the backwardness of editorial boards in not insisting that authors and referees complete these functions, so that a published paper can be described in an indexed abstract journal at the same time that it is published. The cost of speeding up publication and indexing to a few weeks or less is only a small percentage of the cost of the research involved, and a still smaller percentage of the potential increase in research value resulting from this step.

THE FUEL OF SCIENCE

Observation. The number of potential scientists is very small and it is important to find them and make sure that their talents are not wasted.

In very round numbers there are about 1,000 American research astronomers, 20,000 physicists, 100,000 chemists. About one-tenth of these in each field produce almost all of the creative research and publications. Some recent studies on manpower and intelligence suggest that these figures could not be more than doubled if all potential male students of these fields actually entered them, although they might be increased considerably by finding ways for talented women to take up such professional careers, or perhaps by preschool enrichment of children at ages 1 to 5, which is now believed to have dramatic effects on curiosity and intelligence.

Translated into birth-rate, these studies would mean that in a population of roughly 200 million, only about 20 future astronomers are born per year, 400 future physicists, and 2,000 future chemists. Perhaps another 1,000 or 2,000 research biologists. It is these few who can invent radar or DDT or discover the nature of molecular diseases.

Inference. Millions of dollars per year are justified in finding, supporting, and educating potential research scientists. This should include support of those from underprivileged families who would otherwise find it impossible to finish high school or go to college.

Inference. Their value to the nation is tens of thousands of times greater in a research laboratory than drafted into the army, as so many of them still are.

Inference. Research productivity could be almost doubled by educating brilliant girls for science and making scientific careers feasible for them.

THE FIREPLACE: THE INSULATED AGENCY

The reaction needs a reaction vessel, the seedling needs a compost heap, the match must be held between cupped hands. The fire is most efficient in a fireplace or stove where it will not fall or be knocked apart. Science needs to be somewhat shielded from the continual rearrangements of public opinion, the blasts of special purpose, and the rain of legislative disapproval.

A fire must be allowed an undisturbed period of the order of several reaction-times in order to "catch." After a rearrangement has been made, a similar period must elapse before the effect on growth and direction can be certain, and a much longer period before the fire can reach its full brilliancy and efficiency. A coal fire may need kindling for a half-hour in order to catch, and two hours to reach maximum heat. It should be no surprise if a research program takes a year or two to catch, and three to five years or more to reach its maximum effectiveness.

Inference. Research personnel must be shielded from non-intellectual duties.

After the science administrator has gotten good men and given them facilities, his function and his first concern should be to shield them from all housekeeping problems. Meetings, written reports, orders, memoranda, time sheets, and accounting must all be cut. A chain-reaction is not a bank. Research time is more precious than pennies or records.

The cost of pleasant offices and salaries, teaching and laboratory assistants, secretaries, accountants, draftsmen, ample library and shop facilities—and administrative assistants to keep these services competent and unobtrusive—is small compared with the twofold or fourfold increase in intellectual productivity which they make possible. It is interesting how many of the great nineteenth-century inventors and scientists had a shadow—a skilled and faithful assistant for many years, who carried out the projects, the errands, and the services, acting as a second pair of hands to free the other mind for thought.

Efficient services of this kind reduce the critical size. Better five scientists with these services than ten without.

It is important to keep a research group informed of changes and decisions that affect their work, and to make them feel that their advice is welcome, but the science administrator must resist the democratic urge for employee participation and for spreading his responsibility onto committees.

Inference. Personal research contracts and organization contracts should run for two or three years before critical review, and for considerably longer before maximum output can be expected.

Inference. Inquiries and official visits, explanations and justifications, should be rare and brief, limited by custom if not by statute. Changes of policy and reorganization should be very rare, and well-planned in advance.

We cannot dig up a plant every day to see how its roots are growing. Only a fool would take coals out of a fire regularly to see how they were burning. We must judge research, like fires and trees, by the subtle steady changes in the output.

Inference. Research must be run by an insulated agency.

This is the central reason for the success of the basic civilian research programs of the Office of Naval Research and of the Atomic Energy Commission in the years just after World War II. Being associated with vast military programs, these civilian projects were assembled and sustained on the one hand by the keen military appreciation of the value of basic research; and on the other hand were protected against sudden financial shock, thanks to reservoirs of military funds and the provision in some cases for three-year and five-year contracts. They were also protected against the sudden hazards of legislative investigation, thanks to the great scope of the associated organizations, which made it likely that the little civilian projects would be brushed over in any scrutiny and not forced to justify their relevance to the sovereign State of X—or the Senator from Y—or the national objectives of Z—. The consequence was that science made great leaps in the supported fields; this policy produced intellectual chain-reactions more important than nuclear reactors themselves.

In the other direction, we can see from this "principle of insulation" one reason for the low scientific output of many state universities where these schools are limited to one-year budgets and are closely dependent on legislative favor. This also helps us understand the low output in many government laboratories where red tape is standard and where reorganizations and changes of policy are frequent.

No research laboratory can be successful which is too closely tied to elections or legislatures, either politically or financially.

Such agencies as the National Science Foundation need to be protected against these hazards. Compared to the postwar ONR, the Foundation stands naked and exposed on a wind-swept political plain. In England, the strength and effectiveness of the universities and their research has been due in no small measure to the strength and independence of the University Grants Commission, which is provided with funds by Parliament but is above any political interference with the distribution of them. The long-run scientific effectiveness of the NSF will depend on its success in attaining a similar strength and independence here.

An insulated agency may not be a good one; but to be good, it must be insulated.

Most of the inferences I have made here are not particularly novel. They have been drawn by other scientists and by various administrators and agencies. But the usual collection of observations and heuristic rules, supported by bits and pieces of evidence, takes on new force when it can be unified in this way by the chain-reaction idea. To see the pieces all together as different aspects of the familiar problem of how to build a fire, is to see them in a new light and to understand their relationships very much better.

I think many of the conclusions drawn here about the best organization of scientific research will have close counterparts in other social chain-reacting fields. And I suspect there are many other areas where this kind of detailed use of a physical analogy such as fire, will lead to valuable new understanding of what would otherwise be complicated and difficult problems.

*One idea can be developed into a chain-reaction that
changes the world.*

Seed Operations

In the last chapter, we discussed social chain-reactions of the
steady-state or slowly growing kind. Let us now go on to examine
some social chain-reactions of the rapidly growing or exploding
kind, to see what initiates them and what makes them grow.

The conditions for growth of a chain-reaction are that it must
have an energy supply to maintain itself, and that its "control
rods" must be "pulled out" so that the multiplication factor,
k, in successive steps of the reaction is greater than 1.00. And it
has to be started off by some first step, or trigger.

Evidently there are two foci of power for the manipulation of
a chain-reaction: a control rod or a gas pedal; and in the explosive
cases, the initiating event represented by the trigger, the push
button, or the detonator cap. These are the insignificant spots
where a touch releases, and a pre-set structure directs, the energy
resources of the whole system.

Tons of effort of the wrong kind or at the wrong place may
produce little effect. Many explosives, for example, can be heated
to the melting point, dropped, or even hammered, with little
danger. But a tiny stroke of the right kind at the right place—
a scratch on the detonator cap—sets everything off.

By working at these foci of power, we amplify our small efforts
enormously. In engineering, we no longer build pyramids with

the direct human energy of a hundred thousand slaves dying under the whip. Instead, we make machines and gasoline engines and dynamite; and then a few hundred men who know how to turn an ignition key or push a pedal can create a Boulder Dam or a Grand Coulee, a pyramid of concrete that slides down and solidifies across a river. And this in turn is only another amplification point and control rod, for it is used to manage thousands of times its own volume of water—under the guidance, perhaps, of one civil servant in shirt sleeves who sits in front of a panel of buttons.

To us, these amplifications piled on amplifications are obvious —the familiar technical braggadocio of our times. To the Pharaohs building their pyramid tombs, they would have been obvious, too—obvious lies.

Yet I think we are now becoming aware that there are areas other than engineering where we can create a similar chain-reacting amplification of our efforts. Chain-reactions can be seen in the exponential growth of science or new industries, in the spread of a new alphabet or number system or the adoption of a new social idea. And a little consideration shows us that these social chain-reactions, like physical chain-reactions, must and do have initiating points and control rods. Somewhere in each one, if we are intelligent enough to find it, there is a focus of power where a small effort will be amplified out of all proportion, because it sets off the self-amplifying channeling of great intellectual, social, or economic energies into certain directions with a k greater than 1.00. A patent or reward system to generate a steady flow of new inventions. A new flavor to sell a soft drink. At these points, a dollar spent to change k today can create effects after a short time that many thousands of dollars spent directly could not do or undo.

Conversely, the attempt to initiate a chain-reaction when k is less than 1.00 is wasted effort. The realist says: You can't oppose the system; and he is right. The idealist says: I may change k; and he is right. Evidently the realistic idealist needs to put his effort not into trying to oppose chain-reactions that are already going, and not into trying to initiate reactions that won't go; but into trying to change k in each case.

BIOLOGICAL CHAINS

Medicine affords a good illustration of all these principles. For a century now, medical research (itself a chain-reaction) has been the control-rod system for the microbial chain-reaction multiplication that causes disease and epidemics. It is trivial to sterilize the drinking water or to be vaccinated. But it is deadly to neglect these precautions and get typhus or diphtheria or any of a dozen other diseases. These precautions change k, for diseases that could not be cured afterwards with thousands of times the effort. "An ounce of prevention is worth a pound of cure" connects two different times in a chain-reaction.

And these diseases are not to be cured by what in classical medicine seemed to be the direct attack—not by bleeding or poultices, or handwashing or continence or steam inhalations, or diet or fresh air or high altitudes. We now see that these procedures are mostly nostrums and placebos, for they do not interrupt any step in the multiplication of the microorganisms and have little effect on the k of the process. For this reason, the doctor today has become less and less an adviser and more and more an agent of a k-changing research laboratory.

One or two virulent bacteria are enough to multiply and to kill, if their k is greater than 1.00; but a massive infection, with millions of microorganisms, may die away harmlessly if their k is less than 1.00. (Is not the same true of new ideas and of political efforts?) So our sharing of bacteria on telephones and on door handles and in kissing causes few diseases as long as diet and health keep k below 1.00 in the individual and as long as public-health measures also keep our general social k for bacteria less than 1.00.

A healthy person or a medically healthy society is not healthy because it is uninfected. It is healthy because it resists infection, because its control rods are functioning against undesirable chains.

We are familiar with control rods throughout the biological world. The farmer of plants and animals controls their multiplication factors. With wild animals, the numbers can be regulated by game commissions, by the simple methods of offering bounties or controlling the length of the hunting season. When rabbits became a pest in Australia, they were destroyed by injecting a few of them with a virus disease that multiplied still more rapidly.

In the case of human reproduction, we have now suddenly pushed in the control rods that limit our diseases and pests, and pulled out those that expand our food supply and protection from hazards. This has insulated our own reproductive reaction from its earlier losses, suddenly increasing our k over the world from a value near 1.00 up to almost 2.00 per generation. Our reproduction has gone out of control, and threatens to expand within a few short decades—in fact, has expanded already—to an absolutely inhuman density of people over the world. Our forests and walking places have disappeared, our animals are mangy in zoos, our beaches are covered with oil and candy wrappers, our rivers are unfit to swim in, our air is unfit to breathe, and we are stacked in tenements and tubes instead of living among forests and fields, largely because we are already too numerous, even in America, by two or three times.

What to do? Evidently we need to "push in" some new control rods. One of them would be further research on cheaper and more universal and pleasant birth-control methods; and if we put our minds to it, I believe we might devise even more subtle and powerful incentives and methods.

For lack of a nail, the battle is lost. For lack of a one-cent birth-control chemical we can eat every day, human civilization can be lost.

ECONOMICS AND WAR

In economics, bankers and the officials who control interest rates are in focal positions. An interest rate of 4 per cent means that some k, for the multiplication of money or goods, must be greater than 1.04 per year. A fraction of a per cent up or down in Federal Reserve rates becomes multiplied and amplified, exponentially, changing the prospects of profit or loss over the whole country. Projects may be initiated, projects dropped, and great effects produced in the economy within a few months.

I spoke earlier of "socio-technical inventions" as seed operations that generate great social and economic effects. Money, the coin itself, was a tiny invention, yet it multiplied itself as it multiplied commerce. The invention of movable type multiplied itself into mass education and world communication. Watts' tea kettle multiplied itself into the industrial revolution. One might even think of the ballot as a little Greek invention that multiplied itself into the democracies. Who knows what other small convenient social tools await invention, "triggers" that would be amplified by tremendous social energies, ready to beautify our neighborhoods or curb crime, ready to expand and shake continents? Inventing the right devices of this kind and determining that they will produce change in the desired directions would be one of the most effective things a social reformer could undertake.

In war, the crucial foci of the economy stand out very clearly. They are the "bottlenecks" of production, like machine tools or rare metals; or the prime targets of strategic bombing, such as locomotives, ball-bearing plants, oil refineries, and shipping, whose destruction can affect the k of a whole industrial society. Knowing which of these control rods to push in may be worth more than a dozen front-line assaults.

The enemies of the United States in World Wars I and II seem to have had a genius for this strategy in reverse. Instead of pushing in her control rods, their first gesture was to pull out the most important ones, with the sinking of the *Lusitania* in the first war and the attack on Pearl Harbor in the second. The southern attack on Fort Sumter that started the Civil War showed the same inverted genius. Each time, it turned out to be as simple as putting a revolver to one's head and pulling the trigger. They didn't know it was loaded.

What starts wars? Does not a pre-war situation show strong similarities to a chain-reaction, in the growth of mutual antagonism across a boundary? I arm. He arms more. I arm still more. Like dogs circling, we cannot remain ambivalent. Our old biology drives us to a decision. All or none. There is a multiplication factor; k is greater than unity and antagonism grows with time.[1]

The problem of avoiding war is the problem of finding the social control rod, the trivial steady pressure at some focal point, which will keep this k below 1.00.

It occasionally stays below 1.00 for long periods because of factors we can only guess at, as in Penn's peace with the Indians, or the long peace between Switzerland and her neighbors, or the Canadian-American peace. It occasionally rises above 1.00 in surprising situations such as civil wars, where we might have expected the ties of language and economics and a common government to help keep the k for antagonism rather low. It is easy to see that an acceptable and equitable legislature and court system offering some relief to all factions is a device for the dissipation of antagonism, to keep k below unity. A good parliament is an envy balancer and a hate absorber. Where every complaint and every offense has immediate adjustment by mechanisms of information and accommodation that reduce disagreement instead of amplifying it, hatred does not multiply.

In the absence of an international peace-keeping machinery capable of absorbing antagonism in this way, is there a unilateral control rod against war? Is it economic pressure? Coca-Cola? Underground agents? Demonstrations of strength? A "hard line"? Or do these increase k? Whether such control rods exist, how to manipulate them, and whether we would want to manipulate them, are central questions. One may imagine an especially intelligent Diplomatic Service setting up Operations Research on the physical, economic, biological, psychological, and mathematical problem of finding the strategy and tactics of reducing the k for war in an acceptable way. It would be more effective than disarmament, which only tries to clean out the abscess without stopping the self-multiplying chain of infection.

CIVIL AMPLIFICATION

In politics, are there push buttons of persuasiveness which a minority group can use to get its opinions heard and adopted?

Obviously a revolutionary group may seize the administrative foci of power; there is a whole "science" of such strategy. Obviously, rich men in a democracy may try to own and control newspapers and other media, so that they can control the multiplication factor of what other public figures say.

But sometimes, groups outside the power structure can initiate amplifying chains. In the legislative field, two remarkable achievements were the adoption by the U.S. Congress of a pay-as-you-go Federal Income Tax system as a result of the almost single-handed effort of one man, Beardsley Ruml; and the adoption of a civilian Atomic Energy Act partly in response to the concentrated effort of a few hundred atomic scientists.

Among projects of such novelty and scope, these measures were remarkable for their bipartisan support and speed of adoption. This came about, I believe, because of careful advance planning in each case to meet or remove anticipated objections, because of careful legislative tactics, and because the programs were pushed by persons who stood to gain nothing by them. This intelligent attention to detail resulted in an enormous amplification of the effectiveness of the individual advocates of the legislation over what they might have had as members of more conventional political action groups. It goes to show that political effectiveness for intelligent citizens is not as hopeless as it has sometimes been represented, provided they follow certain chain-reacting principles of action.

Not all new laws are technical measures like these. Most require a more general swell of public opinion. How can a minority group with a particular program of action enlarge its popular base? How can it be most persuasive in the chain-reaction of ideas that makes up opinion? Is there an effective method—a positive counterpart to Thoreau's "civil disobedience"—that we might call "civil amplification"?

Certainly there have been instances where generally peaceful persuasion has amplified minority opinions irresistibly and converted them into law within a generation or two. One such case, I believe, was the spread of antislavery sentiment in the North before the Civil War. There were certain sources of social energy in this chain-reaction, such as the economic self-interest of the manufacturing states, and the new egalitarian ideas, along with an increased Romantic sensitivity to suffering which made the public more susceptible to books like *Uncle Tom's Cabin*. But I also think the growth of the abolitionist movement was greatly accelerated by the deliberate steady pressure of one enlightened group on an emotional focus of power. I refer to the abolitionist ministers and their forerunners, who called into being a religious and humanitarian concern for one's fellow man which had scarcely a precedent in the public opinion and laws of earlier times. It marked a new milestone for the human spirit. This group transformed emancipation from commercial convenience to a magnificent and irresistible human necessity derived by irrefutable logic from the Christian ethic.

These men, a few thousand in their weekly pulpits, taught by who knows what still smaller band of Christian reformers in their theological schools, created a great popular movement within a single generation. They made their attack on slavery heard; then debated; then respected; then a holy crusade.

This instance of religious-social amplification might be compared with the role of the Church in triggering off the Crusades in the Middle Ages, or with that of Richelieu and Father Joseph in stimulating the Wars of Religion. But I think it is more remarkable because the northern ministers were individualists who found themselves with a common cause, and had no central ecclesiastical hierarchy to organize their campaign.

It is an interesting question what group, if any, in our own times would correspond in authority and potential social power to these abolitionist ministers. *That* group would be the one for a minority to convince!

There were other cases in the last century where radical opinion became transformed into accepted law within a generation. This was true of labor unionization and of many reforms of the Fabians and other Socialists. But these are less remarkable because many of these reforms finally came to be, quite obviously, in the self-interest of the majority, so that adoption was almost inevitable.

The case of the Woman Suffrage movement is an interesting exception. The source of social energy for this reform must have come partly from the growth of factories and from the mass conscription of the wars, along with the education of women, all of which helped put women into paid independent jobs and into positions of leadership. And the early bluestockings certainly tried loudly and sometimes violently to initiate the chain-reaction. But the crucial focus of power in this particular struggle was—obviously—in the home. Once the idea had been publicized, there came to be an interested party and advocate for the emancipation of women in every household. After a generation of partisan mothers, the children thought that letting women vote was radical, gallant, and inevitable. It swept the world.

EFFECTIVENESS

What determines which of the many different opinions and measures of seers and reformers at a given time will become amplified into social realization?

Clearly most of the successful ideas are those that "work with the grain," that are reinforced by some social energy supply or social pressure. They are the ones that describe a succession of steps that many men want to take for one strong reason or another. The directions of success are therefore not arbitrary but must conform, say, to the economic energies or the egalitarian sympathies of the times.

The advocate of change who cannot couple his efforts to such a social energy supply is wasting his time. He would do better to write for posterity, or to transfer his efforts to some other cause where they will have a better multiplication factor in his time.

At the end, Simón Bolívar said, "I have plowed the sea." It was not quite true, but it is the lament of a man who has fought a linear battle instead of an exponential one. The first rule for reformers should be: Fight no linear battles. Find the focus. If you are really bringing forward what is good for society, there must be a way to translate it into the daily goods of men, where one push will be all that is needed. If the chain-reaction is ready to begin, a single letter to the President, a single trip to the Finland Station, will be enough.

For it is misrepresenting the problem of social change to view it simply as the struggle of enlightened minority against hostile majority. Far more often, the majority would like to do better but does not know how. They would like to reduce tension or increase diversity or give the greatest good to the greatest number, and they might even agree that if they ever get to that point, it would mean more prosperity and happiness for everyone and no loss for anybody; but they do not see how to get there without an intervening dislocation and effort and sacrifice; so they do not believe it can be done, whether they want it or not. In such a situation, what intelligent men can do is to work out a path of less dislocation—a new channel of change—along which the social energy of these true majority wishes can make itself effective without climbing such difficult barriers. Biochemical intelligence gets around the direct barriers all the time with its catalysts and enzymes; why not social intelligence? The main business of an enlightened minority is not fighting the majority but showing them how.

The vocal minorities of our time often seem to have a talent for ignoring these principles of effectiveness as well as other amplifying tactics that would increase their success. They push very hard on ineffective pedals, barely keeping their k equal to 1.00 so that they do not dissolve entirely. There is the weekly meeting of the dedicated discussion group, full of independent girls in search of companionship. There is the mass meeting with hand-painted posters. There is the high-minded little magazine which must keep appealing to generous angels for money.

I see many of these groups spending their energies on immovable minds, firm friends or firm opponents, rather than on adolescents and the hurt and unsure, ripe for persuasion. They work on Large Projects, rather than on the small successes that can make decision and action concrete and immediate. Yet with all this, they are too practical, without enough long-range thought for "when this child grows up" and when the ideas of a new generation displace the old. They are too cerebral, without enough use of bright and inspiring sexual and religious forces. They are too self-contained, without enough independence to split in two, and split again, like the early Christians, when the group becomes larger than a dozen or so.

There are so many of these principles of strategy and tactics untouched by the usual minority organizers that again a whole Operations Analysis is indicated. I suspect that the historical success of certain minorities is due to their having had leaders like the Apostle Paul or Brigham Young, who understood and preached and practiced many of these amplification techniques.

Any minority in our time that carries out a modern analysis of this kind and uses it will quickly assume an influence far beyond its numbers. This may be, in fact, the explanation of the recent startling expansion of Right-wing groups in many cities and towns throughout the United States. This is one reason why it is so important to state these techniques of minority super-effectiveness explicitly, so we will not begin to be swamped by these or other minorities using sophisticated methods we are unfamiliar with. If there can be a widespread understanding of these social chain-reaction amplification methods, there is a better chance that various opposing groups will be able to use them and to confront each other in the marketplace of ideas so that we will have a choice of those whose techniques as well as their purposes are acceptable and useful to us.

Today our prejudice, vanity, love, and ambition are already being manipulated hourly, not by amplifiers for a cause, but by amplifiers designed by market research for commercial profit. It is not clear that any social or political reform group can ever keep up with this highly paid and self-maintaining Operations Analysis; but if they do, many of us might find it a pleasure to be courted and moved, for a change, by those who think they have something serious or inspiring to lead us to, instead of by those who only want to sell us washing powder. Possibly a competition of social persuasion methods among minorities would even lead to a competing proliferation of useful social inventions that might show us how to translate many of our long-range social goals into daily personal incentives. A widening of the strategy of minorities to touch and fulfill deep motivations and responses, as commercial advertisers always try to do, must become, in the long run, a widening of the area of life in which we understand how our chain-reactions link us to each other and to the future and determine our welfare and happiness.

THE FLUX OF CHANGE

Yet social and political reform groups still need to be reminded that the most important control rods for social and political change lie outside their usual sphere of action. These control rods are at present being pulled out and pushed in in a necessary technical sequence whose laws of development we have hardly begun to understand, and they produce random social changes, now this way, now that, which we can only partially anticipate. The control rods I refer to are those of technical invention and discovery.

It would be impossible to weigh the human values of Henry Ford and, say, Henry Ward Beecher or the Fabian Socialists in the same balance. But the multiplied influence of Henry Ford and a handful of his competitors—on transport, farming, industrial design and productivity, labor relations and living conditions, the size of cities and the size of the world, the structure and mores of the family, national development and resources, the rehabilitation of underdeveloped countries, international disputes, foreign policy and war—in all these aspects of life, the influence of the few creators of the gasoline engine and the motorcar has been far beyond the power of all the humanitarian ministers and all the socialist reformers to add or to detract.

Can we not say the same for a dozen inventions of the last hundred years—the electric light, television, DDT, atomic power, automation, or oral contraceptives?

Can any reformer or planner really play a sweet sonata of social improvement among these firecrackers? Morals are affected more by the comfort of cars than by counselors; politics more by productivity than by pamphlets; peace more by new energy sources than by congresses of diplomats. The abolition of slums may be accelerated by invention of better prefab construction methods; or retarded by unemployment resulting from automation. One small country may be impoverished by the competition of new synthetics while another grows rich exporting plant products for a new drug.

Alas for the Women's League for Family Living. Movies broke up the family. Three cheers for the Women's League for Family Living. Television has restored it. One bad, one good? No. Both are copies of light signals. Just different duplication methods leading to different economics of distribution. Alas and/or hooray for the photoelectrons. Alas and/or hooray for the Women's League.

All plans and work for the future, as in building a house, for example, are based on imperfect knowledge. This does not stop us; we do the best we can. We create the future by planning and working for it. But what I am saying is that today large social or political planning for more than 10 or 15 years ahead is much less sure of its consequences than building a house. It is based on knowledge that is not only imperfect, but non-existent. It is like being in a small boat in a rip tide with whirlpools. No action has the long-run effect expected, because of our diverse chain-reacting technological expansions. What seems terribly important to do today may turn out in 20 years to be trivial compared to several other initiation steps we should have started. The man of goodwill interested in social progress might do better to turn his talents and energy into the analysis of these effects of invention, to improve their predictability; or into some other field where the rules do not keep changing and where he can produce something of permanent value.

SEED OPERATIONS

But my main object in making this critique of the more familiar methods of social amplification has been to show the contrast with a much more effective method of using intelligence to solve the problems of society. This consists of the deliberate use of seed operations, technical inventions, or social inventions, that work with the developing social and technical forces of the time to produce a tremendous amplification of the initial effort. It is like dropping a tiny seed crystal for "nucleation" into a supersaturated chemical solution. The seed shows the way to go, so to speak, and the excess energy of the whole solution suddenly crystallizes out in the direction indicated.

Technical inventions, like those of Henry Ford, are cases where very often the full social results are not intended or foreseen. But many of the successful social seed operators have known quite precisely what they were doing. We have already discussed the seminal achievements of a number of these, Bacon, Franklin, the designers of the Constitution, Baruch, Ruml, Szilard, the atomic scientists. We should add the name of Thomas Jefferson, who founded an academy, made agricultural reforms, and invented decimal weights and measures that spread throughout the world (though not, alas, to the United States). And of Daniel Burnham, the almost single-handed deviser of the great system of lake front parks in Chicago.

"Make no little plans," said Burnham. "They have no power

to stir men's souls." It is the remark of a man who *intended* to initiate social chain-reactions.

The name of Leo Szilard has been mentioned several times, but his many astonishing amplification operations are not as well known as they should be, and a list of them may give an idea of how such a man works. As a scientist, Szilard made key initial contributions to information theory, to radiochemistry, to atomic energy (where he held some of the basic patents), to molecular biology, and to the theory of enzyme action, of aging, and of memory; and at the end of his life he helped initiate the Salk Institute of Molecular Biology in La Jolla.

All of Szilard's social and political efforts are not known, because he usually preferred to work through and with others, from behind the scenes, but some of his seed operations with great social consequences that are already apparent have been described by Alice Kimball Smith and by Eugene Rabinowitch.[2, 3] They include:

1. Persuading British and American atomic scientists to secrecy in 1939–1940.

2. (With Eugene Wigner) Getting Einstein to write the letter to Roosevelt that started the American atomic energy project in 1940.

3. Trying to get the Franck Report and the Szilard Report to the President in 1945, to plead for international demonstration of atomic bombs before any military use.

4. Mobilizing scientists and Senators in 1945 to prevent hasty adoption of the May-Johnson Bill for military control of atomic energy.

5. (With Harrison Brown) Getting Foundation support of oral-contraceptive research increased more than twentyfold in 1951, to help solve the world population problem.

6. Helping found the annual East-West Pugwash conferences in 1952 for unofficial examination of what science could do to help ease international tensions.

7. Founding the Council for a Livable World in 1961–1962 as a channel for transmitting to Washington, much more effectively, the community sentiment for a less rigid and more enlightened foreign policy.

There is a test that could be called the "Streetcar Test" for measuring the degree to which any individual has personally affected history. It consists of asking: Would world history have been appreciably different if this man had been run over by a streetcar at, say, age 10? For most kings and presidents—and most scientists—the answer is no. If they had not lived, their places would have been taken by others with substantially similar opinions and policies and discoveries. But for some men—Lenin, Gandhi, Hitler, Churchill—the answer is obviously yes. The state of great sections of the world would have been almost inconceivably different today if any one of these men had not lived.

Many who know best the work of Szilard, and appreciate its spreading consequences, feel that his name must be put in this same company. Certainly it would be hard to name another who has successfully initiated such a series of projects of such central importance to the human race and with such enormous multiplier factors. With his essential role in atomic energy, population control, and disarmament, it may be that in a hundred years or so he will be regarded as perhaps the most influential individual of our times in his crucial initiating contributions to human power, human stabilization, and human happiness.

It is obvious that seed operations of such importance are not easy. It takes intelligence and foresight, hard work and accurate judgment of men, the inspiration of loyalty in a few, patience and commitment, and an odd blend of certainty and self-sacrifice, to carry such a project over the initial hump of persuasion. The seed operator may be anathema to good committee members, because he raises bizarre questions and initiates strange analyses and procedures that make extra work whose value is hard to explain. He may get the blame without the credit. Seed operation is like pulling a trigger. The hammer hurries to say, I did it; the powder says, I did it; the bullet says, I did it; and they are all correct, as well. But when it works, and the "mustard seed that was the tiniest of all seeds becomes a great tree, and the birds come and lodge in the branches," the result is worth it.

Szilard seemed to be a kind of complex Newton in his principles of amplified social effectiveness and his remarkable series of successes in applying them. Fortunately for all of us, he was on the side of the human race. It will be of the greatest interest to have a complete publication of his collected papers in the near future, to see whether he set these principles down explicitly in a form others can use in shaping human society closer to meeting universal human desires.

Anyone interested in the science of society or of politics will find, I think, in these many overlapping and interacting chain reactions, their triggers and control rods, and principles of seed operation, a subject almost ready for mathematical analysis, prediction, manipulation, and improved design.

Socio-technical inventions, symbols, and counters may be the most subtle and effective directors of social effort.

Limits, Balance, and Guidance in Society

The physical scientist or engineer wandering through societies sees things with strange eyes. Once, for a year or two, I fancied I saw every social interaction as FEEDBACK, in capital letters, and I made a catalog of all the instances I saw. "Feedback" is a word that comes up regularly today, thanks to Wiener and Shannon and the other theorists of information, communication, and "cybernetics." It is no longer a cant word but has become an everyday term needed for describing any amplification or stabilization process in the physical, biological—or social—sciences. In particular, there seems to be no synonym to take its place in describing a quantitative control mechanism either of the electronic sort or of the biological self-regulating or cybernetic sort. Our generation will simply have to carry this idea as far as it can, just as a hundred years ago political and social theorists like Spencer and Bagehot had to carry their dramatic new term "natural selection" as far as they could. Perhaps the modern sociologist or political scientist, with his own specialized vocabulary, will someday find it illuminating to see how many aspects of society can be described in this new language of the electronics engineer.[1]

There is a large family of social relationships where the idea of "negative feedback" seems especially important. We have talked in earlier chapters of "positive feedback" in society, where each motion away from a starting point makes the next step more inevitable, producing an accelerating or amplifying process. It is the existence of such triggers and amplifying mechanisms that have made me speak of our world as a "plastic society," one which has been molded—or contorted—by a historical succession of accidental if not vicious trigger actions, but which is potentially under the control of human intelligence if we can learn to understand such trigger or seed operations and pay attention to the individual feedbacks and forces that amplify a result in the desired direction.

But it would be wrong to suggest that every aspect of society is unstable and sweeps wildly from one amplified result to another, even though anyone who has lived through the last fifty years might think so. Society has its stabilities, too. The Democratic donkey and the Republican elephant are still with us after a hundred years, and they still divide elections with strange equality. This is a stability by no means trivial, as we shall see. And there are others. This must mean that some aspects of society have negative feedbacks, with any deviation away from a stable point tending to be self-correcting, coming back "automatically" toward "normal" again and again.

BOUNDARIES

In a physical flow system, or a social flow system, one place where such stabilities can occur is at the physical or social limits of an amplification process—the edge of a match flame, for example, or the outer surface of a tree. These are points where the growing process encounters some limits of energy supply or organization, although energy and materials may be flowing continually up to these limits and away again. Of course, stability is a relative matter, and on another time scale, as, for instance, in a "time-lapse" motion picture, these stable limits may appear to be dynamic limits, growing or decreasing rapidly with time.

Stability takes a somewhat different form in the cases where two dynamic processes intersect or oppose each other. Where the dynamic equilibrium between the two processes is well-balanced, this may produce quasi-static boundaries with true long-term stability, or what the chemist or flow engineer might call "steady-state boundaries." (A balance between static processes is called "equilibrium"; a balance between flow processes is called a "steady state.") Such steady-state boundaries are familiarly seen in the steady internal and external structures of a waterfall, of a match flame, and of a living cell, and, I believe, in many structures in society. They have the characteristic that their form is maintained even though volumes of energy or materials or information may be flowing rapidly across them and through the system. Boundaries created in this way are often very stable, and even a large disturbance of the system—a reduction in the flow of a waterfall, for instance, or a draft of air on the flame of a match—may displace the boundaries but does not obliterate them.

It is evidently important to understand the principles of stability and negative feedback that maintain such steady-state aspects of society—just as important as it is to understand the principles of amplification and positive feedback that produce and direct great social changes when they come. Perhaps a nation could progress smoothly through the most dramatic changes in technology or social or international relations, if legislators and social theorists knew what feedbacks to manipulate in order to stabilize certain reassuring aspects of the social system during these changes.

One instance where a dynamic boundary in society may have been stabilized by the negative feedbacks of boundary limitation is at what might be called the "boundary" of a culture, in the Spenglerian or Toynbeean sense; for example, the boundary of the Roman Empire at any given time. Several such cultures, in the course of their history, seem to have expanded away from their region of origin out to some maximum area of conquest and then collapsed after a term of a thousand years or so. The natural scientist is struck by the resemblance to a chain-reaction with a limited supply of fuel, like a match flame starting up, growing larger and larger, and then going out.

Is there some truth to this analogy? Is there a psychic Spenglerian fuel, just a thousand years' worth for each culture, that gets used up? Or could it be that there is in cultural dynamics a great need for real physical fuel—say, in the old days, the supply of timber that built the houses and ships and chariots, and fed the evening fires for poetry and analysis? There is some evidence in this direction. The Greeks had mighty pines where only olives grow today; the early Roman legends were forest legends; the old Chinese scrolls show densely wooded landscapes where barren hills are now; the early Egyptian tomb paintings show the kings hunting in forests. And in the last stages of all these cultures, conservation measures for the remaining woodland rise high on the list of laws.

I suspect that at any given time the boundary of a culture where negative feedback set in was determined to a considerable degree by technical considerations, and was where the marginal expense of further expansion against hostile nature or man became too great for the energy and construction supply and the associated organizational technology developed up to that time; and that decadence and retreat may have set in as much because of the dwindling of physical energy supply at the center as because of social factors.

Even the psychological changes in Toynbee's cultures during their life cycle follow reasonably from the changes in the availability of structural timber and fuel, as anyone might guess who looks at the dependence of national psychologies today upon such factors. The early periods, still among the forests, are times of thrift and integrity, for there is little energy to throw around. The "great" periods are when energy and goods flow in from the colonies and the vast organization of men demands the most competent statesmanship and generalship. Afterwards, conquest becomes too expensive and cumbersome and the greatest men descend to mere talk of greatness, with bitter schemes and decadent laments.

Certainly if energy supply plays a major role, the supposed thousand-year cycle of a culture is not mystical or automatic, but depends on technological details, such as the chain-reaction time-constants for energy exhaustion, which we can identify and study. If this is so, then our world culture today, with its supply of coal and oil and now of atomic energy, will have its future course and prospects altered beyond the possibility of comparison with the wood-and-water cultures of the past.

What sets the boundaries and duration of a culture? Particular supply and feedback mechanisms and their time-constants, whether these are social or physical in origin.

A curiously similar question, on a microscopic scale, is what sets the boundaries—the size of membership—of voluntary weekly or monthly discussion and action groups, such as we find in every community in America? Almost everyone who belongs to a few such groups will have noticed that they tend to run to around twenty to forty active members—at least between membership drives. When there is no strong leader and no strong professional attachment, the size is characteristic of our troops and chapters, whether the members are young or old, of one sex or couples. "Everyone invited," they say, but if you drop in, you will find a steady twenty-five or thirty present, in Epworth Leagues and Missionary Societies, business luncheon groups and Women Voters, student clubs, choral groups, camera clubs, garden clubs, play-reading groups, and many others.

Is this size some racial memory of the size of the ancient troops of apemen? Is it determined by the size of our rooms? Is the number the same in voluntary groups in Europe? In Asia?

Whatever the psychic explanation, we are evidently dealing with a marginal feedback process. Whenever this sort of semisocial American group gets down to fifteen members, the membership committee gets to work; when it gets up to fifty, the committee slacks off, and many members do not come regularly. Consciously or unconsciously, they get less than some marginal level of social interaction or attention they want from the rest of the group, and they go off to join some other group that will give them more.

If this represents some fundamental feedback rule of social behavior, as I suspect it does, then any organization that wants to multiply its political and social mass must find a way to escape these boundary limitations or take them into account; either as labor unions do, by tapping stronger motivations; or as revolutionary organizations do, by tightening the formal structure; or as some primitive religious groups have done, by forcing every chapter to divide in two as soon as it reaches two dozen members.

ELECTION LAWS AND THE STABILIZATION
OF INTERNAL BOUNDARIES

In politics there are some interesting boundaries that are the result—frequently the unexpected result—of adopted rules. I refer to the stabilization of two-party systems and party boundaries in England and America by a majority election law; and the stabilization of many-party systems with their numerous boundaries, in several other countries, by a proportional-representation law.[2]

Consider first the problem of a politician who needs a majority of votes in order to win an election. Where should he choose to stand with respect to the political opinions of the electorate? Evidently as near the center as possible, for if he stands very much to the Right or to the Left or in any other special direction, his opponent has only to be slightly nearer the center in order to win every time; whereas if he stands at the center, he has at least a 50–50 chance of winning, and a little extra charm may tip the balance regularly his way. These considerations are of the kind that are used in the strategic "theory of games," but here they are applied to the game of obtaining votes. If there are three or more candidates in such an election, it is evidently to the interests of the men of the Left and Right to move closer to the center, squeezing out the center man, unless they are held back by other allegiances or by considerations other than winning votes.

Does it work this way? Obviously so. Because throughout the last century in England and America, we usually see only two major parties, with sometimes a third trying to get in. And in national elections, where the judgments of winning strategy are averaged over numerous candidates, the big parties commonly divide the vote almost in half, 50–50, with a 55–45 majority being unusual, and a 60–40 majority being extremely rare.

Such a result over and over again, especially in these rapidly changing times, would be almost impossible to explain except by the operation of some negative feedback continuously pressing the parties toward an equal division. And except in special circumstances, it is not usually an equal division between all on the Right and all on the Left, but is between leading candidates who tend to be near the center, just as the theory suggests. Their policies are often so similar that it is a Tweedledum-Tweedledee choice, difficult to explain to foreigners; but by the same token, there is no great oscillation of most policies when the parties change, and the man who is elected, whichever he is, is able to speak for the center of the whole people.

This beneficial feedback—for so I think it is—grows out of the one or two small words in our laws that provide for election by a majority (or plurality) of the votes cast.

But this situation is in striking contrast to that in countries where they have tried the experiment of "proportional representation" in their election laws, so that a candidate is seated in the legislature essentially by getting a certain minimum number of votes. This scheme was originally put forward to protect the interests of minorities; and protect them it does, but in the process the interests of the majority are continually being defeated. (An example of the amplification of a trigger idea, with disastrous results.) For an office seeker in such a system obviously will do better to take a stand well away from the crowded center and to put himself forward as the candidate of some fringe group where he can gather his minimum vote unchallenged. As a result, there are multiple parties, perhaps 10 to 50 of them; factional boundaries are accentuated; no representative represents any but a small group with some special interest; and government must be conducted by unstable coalitions, and goes begging for a Strong Man to take command.

It is the accentuation of factional boundaries by this feedback mechanism that is particularly unfortunate. Instead of the differences between groups being healed to some degree by the necessity to work together to elect a central candidate, which is what happens in the American and British parties, proportional representation leads to bloc voting, with farm set against city, Catholic against Protestant, wine grower against dairy farmer —with their natural differences, which are real but small, being exacerbated by political invective until they become insurmountable.

This "atomization of the electorate" is not due to some national political instability but is a fault of the method. I have seen it occur in American groups of all kinds that have adopted proportional representation, from student organizations to university senates. In the student movement, I think it is a factor in the creation of splinter groups and their bitterness against each other; and in a university faculty of intelligent men, it leads just as inevitably as elsewhere, to bloc-voting, with theologians set against physical scientists, and undergraduate teachers set against graduate teachers, so that there are few who speak for the faculty as a whole. Is it any surprise that, in a nation, such a system might generate and perpetuate political disputatiousness as a supposed trait of "national character"?

One recent French constitution has gone back essentially to majority elections; it will be interesting to observe whether and how soon this change will produce the expected game-theoretical centralizing effect.

In any new national or world constitution, it is obviously necessary to understand exactly what the election rules and other small rules imply about the strategies of political success, at every level of the structure, from this feedback or game-theory point of view. Change the rules of winning, and you immediately change the strategy and stability of the game. It is not necessary for a constitution to lead to perfect political stability; in fact, a certain amount of instability and atomization should perhaps be designed into any system, so as to avoid ossification and to insure a constant flow of new intellects to the top; but the designers should know what they are putting in, and how, and why.

TIME-CONSTANTS

These political stabilization phenomena, like all feedback systems, are characterized by certain "time-constants" or times of recovery after a disturbance. A good political system, like any stable system with feedbacks, needs several different levels of response to stress and several different time-constants, from sudden responses to long-range adjustments. This "multistability" or "ultrastability" is what Ross Ashby has emphasized in his *Design for a Brain* as a necessary element for survival in a changing world.

In the American political system, different time-constants are provided for in the Constitution, from emergency executive actions to months-long legislative preparation, from the two-year popular feedback in House elections to the six-year terms of the Senate and the lifetime terms of the Supreme Court justices. We will discuss this further in the next chapter, but we may note here that this multistability was a deliberate design. Jefferson once asked Washington why we should need to have a second House in the legislature, that is, a Senate. Washington replied: Why for the same reason that I want a saucer for my coffee, so that the hot legislation can be poured into it to cool before it must be drunk! This is a clear appreciation of the value of time-delays, of shock absorbers, in smoothing out the response of the system.

There is a certain jerkiness in all "flip-flop" systems of the on–off type—or the Democratic-Republican type—but this can be minimized by good design. A good home thermostat is not so coarse that it lets the house get 20 degrees too hot before it shuts off the furnace. The British political thermostat seems designed to be somewhat "stickier" than ours, as the engineer might say, with the party in power given an advantage in holding on until a time of crisis. I think this is the reason why their system appears to make more violent alternations of policy when the parties alternate, which is what this stickiness would lead any designer to expect.

Hamilton spoke of the feedback system of the U.S. Constitution with its "checks and balances" as representing "wholly new discoveries" in social and political design, and it would seem that he was right. But it is time for political theory to note that our age has made some wholly new discoveries itself in the matter of feedbacks and their smoothness. The flip-flop switch or the circuit breaker with its sudden on and off is clumsy compared to the smooth continuous feedback regulation of modern circuitry such as is used in an automatic pilot for a ship or plane. The day of snapback is past.

Perhaps the next development in government might be a similar refinement of our flip-flops in politics, so that fewer functions are left to the strong polarizations and sudden corrections of elections, and more are carried out with smooth continuous feedback regulation for the continuing national welfare. The economic policy of the Federal Reserve system already adjusts interest rates by tiny amounts up or down almost according to economic formula. If the formula were known to be valid and its time-constants were understood, such adjustments could be made automatic and nonpartisan; and there may be many other branches of national planning and policy where such smooth automatic decision-making may someday be possible.

This will not be easy. In the economic area, we have quantitative indices, national inventories, and business indices to show how we are getting along, even though we still argue over what to do about them. But we have few reliable indices of how we are doing in large problems like the Cold War, or the best management of natural resources, or in a number of other areas. Accurate feedback demands accurate quantitative indices.

Yet this way of looking at the matter leads to the thought that in many of our smaller problems it may now be possible to design indices of this sort—"error-signals"—that could indeed show our tactical success in government, day by day, and department by department. Such measures, subject to objective inspection and audit, could then be used in political feedback arrangements to produce much smoother and more continuous self-regulation and maximization of performance.

ERROR-SIGNALS AND INCENTIVES

Wherever there is feedback, there is an error-signal to be fed back, some measure of how far the aim is from the rabbit or the salesman from the quota. We have already described one error-signal, at least by implication—the politician's deficiency of votes. It is the quantitative nature of this signal that makes it possible for the feedback to be so accurate usually in dividing the two-party electorate down the middle.

Another error-signal that strikes the engineering eye is money. Money has many chameleon aspects, as a medium of exchange, as a measure of value, as an index of temporal power. And the anthropologist Geoffrey Gorer emphasizes that many an American is interested in a larger income not for what it will buy, or the number of people he has controlled to get it or can control with it, but as a public index of accomplishment. An impartial index of this kind, if one could be found, would certainly be a most useful error-signal for society.

Happy the nation in which the citizens are rewarded and motivated not for what they inherit or control or have won by gambling or by stock manipulation, but for the degree to which they have enriched other citizens by production! It is probably no accident that the nation in which the anthropologist thinks money serves this index function is the one whose trademark has always been productivity. The first principle of negative feedback is that you cannot maximize something unless you have an index to tell you at every instant how far you are from your goal.

If there were a perfect index symbol for productivity—which money unfortunately is not—the manufacturer who provided maximum satisfaction to many customers at minimum cost to society would grow rich in these symbols. The production manager who dropped behind in his satisfaction–effort ratio would get symbolic warnings from his board of directors. In such an ideal production system, consumer satisfaction would be continuously maximized, because each employee's deviation from his target would be observable and would continuously motivate him to minimize the error, so that the system would be self-guiding. The competition among companies to find what the consumer wants would scatter statistically but would tend to follow changing needs and tastes automatically, as a gun-director follows the target. Inventors would explore the field of human wants continually, searching for new wants to gratify. It is obvious that, in a society where such a symbolic feedback is working properly, industry and commerce will form a chain-reacting system that can produce new processes and new satisfactions many times more rapidly than in a society where the error-signal tends to be sluggish or misdirected or capricious.

The existence of several vigorous productive systems in the modern world shows that fairly good productive self-guidance can sometimes be accomplished with money. Nevertheless, it is clear that money has some drawbacks as an error-signal. For one thing, it does not show the direction and amount of the error (as your eyes do; or a deficiency of votes), so that when profits fall off, a period of hunting is necessary before a production system can locate the target again, a fact well known to toy manufacturers and dress designers. This is the major reason for the growth of market analysis and consumer research, which are supposed to offer much more informative error-signals.

Money is also a poor error-signal for productivity because of its other index functions which, in many societies past and present, have been antiproductive. Wherever its origin is inheritance and its object is ostentation, production disappears. These roles for money can be blocked by inheritance laws and sumptuary laws. Production also plays second fiddle whenever money is made more easily by litigation or by manipulation of the exchange or by restraint of trade. The error-signal continues to point the gun, but to socially unfruitful objects, as the anti-aircraft barrels may track automatically a flight of pelicans or a friendly plane. It is at this point that human intelligence needs to overrule the automatism and stop the firing. A principal economic function of government may be to interfere by law with the pursuit of money in these socially undesirable directions, while taking care not to interfere with its role in the feedback circuits of vital productive processes (except perhaps when it wants to interfere with civilian production in wartime). I suspect that much of the difference in the productivity of different countries, otherwise equally well endowed, is due to these secondary differences in the laws and customs affecting the target toward which money points. Is not this the reason why Europe needs an Anti-Trust Act—to keep money pointing the productive way instead of the accumulative way? And the fall-off in our own productivity in times of great depression or great inflation is not due to any change in the energy or the needs of society, but to the distortions in the meaning and time-constants of our error-signal, money, at these times.

At the levels of the most highly taxed incomes today, money becomes almost purely symbolic as an error-signal. This does not necessarily interfere with its value for this purpose, as long as the paper numbers produce motivation. Even in a society of perfectly equal real incomes, admiration and other social signals would serve to urge a man to action. But since high taxation insulates real income from fluctuations, the old-fashioned types who still believe that money is the proper signal may be led by its insensitivity into all sorts of misdirection of effort and unproductive practices, such as excessive advertising, expense accounts, lobbying, or the too-long continuance of traditional manufacturing methods, side by side with some other practices that are indeed justifiable but only from a larger productive point of view, such as the support of universities. Likewise when money is siphoned off by government to be put into an industrially unfruitful war or public works, it takes on one of its other functions and its value as an industrially productive error-signal is again impaired.

These comments are not made in any partisan spirit but only from an engineering view of the feedback process. A society has to decide for itself what its values are and therefore what its error-signals should be set to indicate, if it wants to maximize the attainment of these values. But this decision should be made consciously and not haphazardly; and the error signal should be adjusted to fulfill its function as intelligently as possible, so that it will operate continuously and efficiently toward the desired aims without periodic "meddling from Washington" and direct conscious readjustment. A government needs the very greatest mathematical, physical, economic, and psychological skills if it is going to be the watchdog over the error-signals and if it is going to sharpen up, and not confuse further, the aiming of the society toward the targets it really desires.

It would be interesting to go on and discuss other error-signals, such as censure and punishment, in our educational and legal flow processes, from a feedback point of view. But I want to turn instead to the relation between public and private error-signals and anticipation times.

VALUE AND ANTICIPATION-TIMES

Let us spend a moment to discuss the good. What kind of actions a person thinks are good for him to do, depends on how long into the future and how far away from his own skin he can anticipate the effects. In a time of revolution and shortage, it may be a good or necessary deed to break into a shop to get bread or clothes or ammunition. Or when it is a question of one life against another, all society agrees that personal survival is a primary good and does not punish the survivor if he was not at fault in picking the quarrel.

It is only in a context of more leisure and wider consideration that these acts of theft and murder become reprehensible. The worst man we know is undoubtedly satisfying some short-sighted interest, and we call the best man best precisely because we believe he is satisfying the longest-sighted and largest interest of all. The difference between a good man and a bad one is not then a difference of intensity of interest. It is a difference of vision.

To know if an act is good, it is therefore necessary to know what its consequences are, spreading out as far as possible into the future. High morality depends on accurate prophecy. But the future becomes more and more uncertain the farther we look. Any prophecy has some half-life or time-constant, beyond which it cannot be trusted more than any random guess. In times of revolution, the half-life is short; in times of peace and stability it is long. This is why the accepted rules of morality change toward the personal and the immediate in times of great emergency and uncertainty. There is little point in sacrificing the present good to the long-run better, if the long run is totally uncertain and is just as likely to be made worse by our sacrifice.

Many of the ancient ethical rules are heuristic value rules, rules-of-thumb, so to speak, to indicate the probable best strategy in such cases where deterministic prophecy becomes simply statistical and fails. (Strategy in the sense of game theory!—as Herbert A. Simon has emphasized in his *Models of Man.*) No one can predict quite what will happen in the long run if you follow the ethical rule and love your neighbor, or if you take a day of rest in every seven. In fact, it is an amusing comic device in fiction to show the well-intentioned man or missionary putting his foot into it, repeatedly, by deviating from the comfortable selfish customs of the world, until his queer behavior has made the pigs run off and the house burn down and the neighbors swear never to touch goodness again. Morality without foresight can be funny when it is not too vicious or tragic.

Nevertheless, the old pragmatic rule of morality says that, on the average, if you have used your intelligence to avoid the predictable evils as far as possible, the unpredictable ones are likely to be less if you err on the side of loving your neighbor rather than hating him. Every intelligent man acts by the predictions of the deterministic prophecy as far as he can foresee; but the man of goodwill chooses the ancient rules of faith and human solidarity in addition, as soon as the prophecy becomes a little dim.

It is obviously important in a technological society to predict the consequences of various acts—this slum clearance, that brinkmanship—as far ahead as possible. And for the times when prediction fails, it is important to reexamine our individual and collective heuristic value rules and strategies—both the old rules of the prophets and the new rules of the atomic diplomats—to see when they are valid and how they should be interpreted for an industrial and international society.

MECHANISMS OF PERSUASION

Is not all this wandering pretty far from our feedback discussion? No, for what this means is that in a stable society, the long-sighted realists and the men of goodwill will get together on mechanisms for persuading the bad or the selfish—I mean, of course, the short-sighted—to fall in with society's predicted long-range needs. More explicitly, they will find or invent feedback mechanisms to transform the social aim into the individual error-signal and motivation. They will devise symbols or organizational structures that convert the long-range good into tangible short-range personal good that keeps any individual, shortsighted or not, from having to sustain his goodness on hope, faith, and promises.

Is the garbage thrown into the streets? .That is unneighborly. Obviously any good man who really loved his neighbors should put his garbage, and perhaps some of theirs, too, into his car and take it to the dump outside of town. (The example is not farfetched: I have seen Christian students give their summers to dig latrines for Latin Americans.)

But today, that would be an absurd test of goodness. We have an easier, better way to deal with garbage. Intelligence foresees the long-run evil (though there are parts of the world where it does not) and pays a compulsory little bit per family to avoid it, so as to put a short-run tangible feedback into the pockets of regular garbage collectors, good men or not. This is more sensible and more automatic than straining our highmindedness in amateur garbage disposal.

It is the same in every social good. Do we fear ignorance in our children and in our neighbors' children? Nowadays we find collective ways to pay teachers, instead of hoping that saintly females will educate the poor out of their overflowing love, as they once had to do. We get better teaching and they get better pay. Do we fear burglars? We decrease their population, we hope, by spending money on youth centers and on police detective work.

Do we want some new product, some new commercial good? The bank makes loans that convert anticipated future income into present construction money and a present automobile for the worker to drive. The more certain the prophecy of income, the lower the interest or discount rate that must be paid to cover the uncertainty. In fact, the motive force for effective social creation could be thought of quantitatively as "discounted anticipated payoffs" that can be bought and sold so as to maximize the individual payoffs that get the job done.

Many of the functions of government today are those of a social bank that now pays to get the job done in the expectation of a future social return. For some of these jobs, private social banks might be possible and apt, as we saw in the 1950's when long-needed superhighways finally began to be constructed as toll roads with private capital. Today, great social banks for supporting higher education—profitably, in terms of return!—might be another bold enterprise and investment of this sort.[3] But a culture that cannot in some way organize this kind of anticipation of future welfare into present rewards for building toward it, is not only a shortsighted and poor culture, it is, in our world, a bad culture for all the people in it regardless of their social values or moral sentiments.

The persuasion of the bad or selfish man is then primarily a question of transforming our long-range good into a short-range feedback for his short-range mind. The first rule for making men good or for making society good is: Never cut off the feedback. Caesar did not make men love him, but he made them serve him, by just this device. The men who shaped the U.S. Constitution assumed, as Hamilton says, that "Men are ambitious, vindictive, and rapacious." They did not make a Utopian appeal to goodness to change this, but tried instead to found a realistic government with feedbacks in it such that the self-interests of individuals would turn themselves automatically to serve the common good; and this was why they succeeded better than any republican government ever before.

TANGIBLE TOKENS

But it is clear that such an exchange of long-range goods for immediate personal goods demands a medium of exchange. Various media are used: the mother's approval, the schoolboy's grades, the scout badges, the soldier's ribbons, the gold watch, the Mason's degrees. And money. You cannot buy goodness; but you can make it pay. The green stuff in the pocket might someday be replaced by something better; but until it is, it is a personal biological feedback far more powerful in getting things done than all our wordy praises.

The difference between unpaid effort and paid effort is like the difference between a compromise and a sale. In a good compromise, each party thinks he got the worst of the bargain; in a good sale, that he got the best of it. Mathematically, it should not make any difference, but psychologically the sale gives a feedback. Each man has something tangible to show for it, and that makes the triumph. If we could apply this principle to international compromises, they would go faster and far more enthusiastically. (Was it not so when the United States bought Louisiana and Alaska?)

This is the difficulty with nonprofit organizations. The secretaries are often cheap; and inaccurate. The administrative officers have nothing immediate to lose by incompetence. Nonprofit hospitals are frequently more expensive than profit-making ones. They have cut off the internal feedbacks that would have maximized their efficiency and made them inexpensive. Having cut off the smaller good, they damage their service to the large good. Never cut off the feedback.

It is evident that many of these organizations whose social value is not measured in money—hospitals, universities, governments, and many other long-range social institutions, and potential social institutions—badly need a nonmonetary medium of exchange to measure how much a particular long-range larger good is worth and how well each person's effort is carrying the group toward it. In the OPA rationing program of World War II, the exchangeable rationing-coupon was a successful device of this sort. And I think this is the reason why the "effectiveness" and "cost-effectiveness" concepts introduced in the Defense Department under McNamara in 1961 had such salutary effects, even though effectiveness is only an index and not an additive symbol of exchange. The invention of usable adult symbols, exchangeable feedback tokens, for such problems would be a valuable exercise for ingenious minds.

What we call a social problem is a situation where habit or complexity or mismanagement or ordinary self-interest is somehow thwarting the larger good. I think it is not optimism, but realism, like Hamilton's, to say we do not consider or use feedbacks sufficiently in such problems in making the larger good tangible in rewarding the small everyday decisions.

For example, I think that even the exploding population problem might be brought under control if we devised better and more satisfying individual feedbacks, both in contraceptive devices and in personal incentives for using them. Research is still needed on much cheaper and more universally applicable and pleasant contraceptive methods, say on chemicals such as some primitive societies may have taken in food and drink, for reducing fertility without reducing sexuality. And the possible development of sexually selective contraceptives, permitting parents to have a boy baby or girl baby as desired, would satisfy everyone's wish and would remove the resistance to contraceptives instantly all over the world, regardless of price, as we have already mentioned.

Various personal incentive feedbacks to help solve the population problem have been put forward, but they are often of exactly the wrong kind. In India, some districts now pay men to be sterilized, but this is both hopelessly inadequate and has the worst of effects on individual psychology and public opinion. The same is true of the suggestion of taxing parents for "excess" children, which is a suggestion sometimes heard in the United States.

But if we turn the problem around and think of giving a bonus of one or two hundred dollars a year every year that a couple, of child-bearing age, does not have an additional child, this would be mathematically equivalent in total economic terms, but would be psychologically much more satisfactory and compelling.[4] National and local governments and school districts would soon find the payment of such bonuses far cheaper than the cost of added schools and roads and city services would have been for each additional child. If the parents are saving society money, why not pay them part of it? This puts the cash benefits of reduced population in the right columns on the books.

And rewards might be far more effective than taxes and punishment. The choice between preventing children and being taxed is a choice of evils, resented in either case. The choice between having children and getting a bonus is a choice of goods, welcomed in either case. We live in a legalistic culture and think only of solving problems by punishment when they could be solved as cheaply and much more easily if we thought of rewards instead.

To get less venal government officers, the thirteen states began to give them a regular salary for the first time. To get better schools, we pay teachers. To get better highways, we form toll road companies. To get fewer children, we must only find an individual reward for it. From this point of view, I think most social problems, and perhaps all, have a technical solution, if we can only think of it—a technical or organizational device, with feedbacks as tangible as money, that will put a piece of the anticipated good in the present pocket.

KEYS AND COINS

This brings us back to our discussion of error-signals. We see that money is only one example of the powerful little unit devices that hold civilization together and make it possible. Turn out the contents of your pocket or handbag and what do you find? Coins, keys, postage stamps, checks, theater tickets, driver's license, credit card, insurance and hospital identity cards, and union cards.

We have spoken earlier of their genesis—these socio-technical inventions—as the seeds that start great social chain-reactions. But you as an individual think of them in a different way. You carry them for efficiency, each one from your point of view a key really, an easy small device that manipulates a larger world. And multiplied in society, we therefore often see them as counters of your interest, as the units that build up whole social structures and operations. It was the coin that made commerce possible; the stamp, extensive mail service; the driver's license and accident cards, safety and insurance; the union card, a wealthy consumer society; the ticket, planned entertainment; the check and credit card, convenience and credit, almost worldwide now.

Our civilization depends on such objective, convenient, interchangeable, countable units as a house depends on bricks. Perhaps we never understand or do anything well until we can break it up or symbolize it in discrete units that we can manipulate separately; otherwise it remains vague and slippery, misleading us into fuzzy thought, or nonthought. The tooth makes the zipper; the soldier, the army; the word, the thought; the neuron, the brain. The boiler and piston multiplied itself into modern industry, and the nuclear reactor into the atomic age. Much of what we call civilized education is the learning to manipulate the key units of reading, writing, and arithmetic. The digit makes the number. The letter makes the word; and 26 letters can manipulate ideas as extensively and exactly—if not, they say, as profoundly—as the thousands of Chinese word ideograms. Perhaps much of our later education would be more effective if it, too, could be reduced to similar symbols and key units. It is because of the simplicity and efficiency of manipulation of these tiny tangible devices that calculation, information, and communication can be fast, objective, factual, and powerful.

And it is some of these small invented units that make possible the sorting, ordering, balancing, and measuring of our values. They are the quantitative media of exchange between anticipated value and present value, that make possible the development of values into real feedbacks with quantitative error-signals, and so into real goods. They are the keys and push buttons, quite literally, that channel the direction and amplification of energy flow in our society. The boy who might have been a burglar becomes a locksmith. The man who might have meditated on his navel meditates on mathematical logic.

The solution to many a social problem may be simple if we can find the necessary small tangible technical or social invention of this type to be the quantitative expression of, or the channel for, the necessary step-by-step personal feedbacks: feedbacks and error-signals that will direct effort accurately to the social ends we want. In the past, such inventions have come haphazardly, although they have been coming more and more frequently. Words were prehistoric, counting was prehistoric, but the alphabet, the coin, the key, and the decimal digit have all been explicit inventions in historic times. The postage stamp is a hundred and fifty years old, the credit card a couple of decades. Perhaps in this complex world it is time to reexamine our little devices of this kind systematically and see what new ones we can now think up whose feedbacks will solve all sorts of problems that we are butting our heads against today with indignation meetings and government committees.

We need multiple inventions, and organizations and rewards for stimulating inventions. We need feedbacks, countable feedbacks, socially sensible and valuable feedbacks that will give us limits where limits are needed, balance where balance is needed, and a goal and measure for our individual efforts that will help us maximize more and more types of social satisfactions for the longer and longer future.

*"Checks and balances" combined freedom and stability
in self-stabilizing social structures. How can
we do it again?*

The Federalists and
the Design of Stabilization

The thirteen independent American states in the 1780's faced a situation curiously parallel to that in the world today. They had just emerged a few years earlier from an exhausting war against a common enemy and they were turning to problems of internal development, but they were divided and confused. They had tried to set up a confederation or union to deal with their common interests and problems, but it had been plagued, as the United Nations is now, by an inability to persuade or coerce the individual states into general adoption of any of its measures, or into contributing their assessed shares of revenue for paying its debts or the wages of its soldiers. Public and private credit had dropped to a low ebb, projects were difficult to plan or finance because of the doubtful future, and the states were agitated by insurrections and secessions. And just as today, two great opposing blocs had formed, the commercial North and the agricultural South; and there began to be talk of forming them into local confederacies of states that would be more successful than the union.

In these circumstances there occurred what I think may be an instructive precedent. A Constitutional Convention of leaders from the various states was called, and certain men began to examine whether there might be some minimum rules of social organization that would promote greater security, stability, and prosperity among these sovereign states. They tried to arrive at these rules from considerations of human behavior and from the historical operation of different systems, reasoning particularly from their own extensive "laboratory experience" of many different provincial governments, state governments, and congresses.

What they came up with was, of course, the famous principle of "checks and balances," or what I think an engineering designer today would call a system of "stabilization feedbacks."

The idea was to set up, at every critical point in the system, some kind of equilibrium between opposing interests and motives so as to have a steady pressure against either the excesses or the defects of policy into which governments were likely to fall. They designed their new Constitution of the United States around this principle in a way which is described in detail in *The Federalist* papers, the series of 85 newspaper articles that Alexander Hamilton, John Jay, and James Madison wrote to try to persuade the public to approve the provisions of the new Constitution.

This emphasis on mechanisms and feedbacks was a new kind of practical political thinking, but it worked, and worked surprisingly well. Although the new Constitution contained many compromises, some of which nearly proved fatal later, as soon as it was adopted it changed the atmosphere and activity of the country almost overnight, healed many of the differences between the states, and made the system a political and economic model of prosperity for the world.

It is fascinating and, I believe, extremely valuable to reexamine *The Federalist* papers today from the point of view of what we now know about engineering design, stabilization, and feedback. I think they may be our greatest text on how social feedback design can be used to achieve social stabilization and effective government, without dictatorship and without limiting the freedom of individuals and groups to differ and to oppose each other and the government and to produce continual changes in the system. They constitute a set of social syllogisms showing

in case after case, theoretically and experimentally, how particular legal or social feedbacks lead to either order or chaos,
stability or instability. What is the phrase, "checks and balances,"
indeed, but an almost equivalent phrase—expressed in the new
technical language of the 1780's—of what we would now call a
system of "negative feedbacks" maintaining a dynamic equilibrium that continually adjusts to various pressures?

It seems to me that this sort of analytical social thinking is
our first political need in the world today. The experienced and
intensely practical authors of *The Federalist* may have understood the operation and importance of feedback mechanisms for
social stability better than many later political philosophers. I
believe their stabilization thinking might therefore be a useful
model for us now in thinking about what new structures and
more sophisticated feedbacks could help us in the larger problem
of keeping peace and prosperity among our more numerous
nations today. Certain characteristics of these early American
designers—their insistence on the value of analysis, their belief
that men could plan rationally a new social design that would
really work, their hardheaded realism and avoidance of mere
"paper prohibitions," their insistence on mechanisms which were
shown to be adequate for dealing with various kinds of stress,
but which were nevertheless minimum mechanisms—may be just
the characteristics we need in thinking about new international
designs.

DESIGN AGAINST INSTABILITY

They knew that what they were doing was a new kind of
deliberate social engineering. They emphasized this in *The
Federalist*:

The novelty of the undertaking immediately strikes us. It has been
shown in the course of these papers, that the existing Confederation is
founded on principles which are fallacious; that we must consequently
change this first foundation, and with it, the superstructure resting upon
it.

The regular distribution of power into distinct departments; the
introduction of legislative balances and checks; the institution of courts
composed of judges holding their offices during good behaviour; the
representation of the people in the legislature by deputies of their own

election: these are wholly new discoveries, or have made their principal progress towards perfection in modern times. They are means, and powerful means, by which the excellences of republican government may be retained and its imperfections lessened or avoided.

They realized from the beginning that they had to design a system that worked, in order to "decide the important question, whether societies of men are really capable or not, of establishing good government from reflection and choice, or whether they are forever destined to depend, for their political constitutions, on accident and force."

And they were confident that the principles they had discovered were real and powerful working principles. In one of his contributions, Hamilton discussed the similarity of their principles to the axioms of geometry: "Though it cannot be pretended that the principles of moral and political knowledge have in general the same degree of certainty with those of the mathematics; yet they have much better claims in this respect than . . . we should be [originally] disposed to allow them."

How did they arrive at these principles? I think it was through their primary concern with avoiding instability. How else is one likely to arrive at a feedback-stabilization mechanism like "checks and balances"? There is no point in designing any system, no matter how good its other objectives, if it is unstable and breaks down when it is most needed. Hamilton said: "It is impossible to read the history of the petty republics of Greece and Italy without feeling sensations of horror and disgust at the distractions with which they were continually agitated, and at the rapid succession of revolutions by which they were kept in a state of perpetual vibration between the extremes of tyranny and anarchy."

In another of the papers, Madison discussed where the instability came from in "pure democracies" such as the old Athenian democracy. His argument about the instability of factions in such a system is one that a game-theorist might use perfectly well today.

From this view of the subject it may be concluded that a pure democracy, by which I mean a society consisting of a small number of citizens, who assemble and administer the government in person, can admit of no cure for the mischiefs of faction. A common passion or interest will, in almost every case, be felt by a majority of the whole; a communication and concert results from the form of government itself; and there is nothing to check the inducements to sacrifice the weaker party or an obnoxious individual. Hence it is that such democracies have ever been spectacles of turbulence and contention; have ever been found incompatible with personal security or the rights of property; and have in general been as short in their lives as they have been violent in their deaths.

After World War II, a number of small countries adopted hopeful new democratic forms, often with the blessing and support of the United States. One after another many of them have dissolved into military dictatorships. Is this due to Communist infiltration, or to latent Fascism, or to inexperience, or to some temperamental inability of certain peoples to form stable governments? I suspect not. I suspect in many cases it is due to their having been given Constitutions without a Madisonian understanding of the sources of instability or a Madisonian design of steady feedbacks to avoid it.

It was instability that Madison abhorred in the early Confederation: "Complaints are everywhere heard from our most considerate and virtuous citizens . . . that our governments are too unstable; that the public good is disregarded in the conflicts of rival parties. . . ."

And the reason why the authors of *The Federalist* feared the breakup of the states into small confederacies was the notorious instability and danger in such arrangements. They said:

A man must be far gone in Utopian speculations who can seriously doubt, that if these States should either be wholly disunited, or only united in partial confederacies, the subdivisions into which they might be thrown would have frequent and violent contests with each other . . . To look for a continuation of harmony between a number of independent unconnected sovereignties, situated in the same neighborhood, would be to disregard the uniform course of human events, and to set at defiance the accumulated experience of ages . . . The causes of hostility among nations are innumerable.

They might have been looking directly at our independent sovereignties today. But it is not clairvoyance; it is an understanding of universal feedback principles in any system with inadequate stabilization mechanisms.

USE OF INDIVIDUAL BEHAVIORAL FEEDBACKS

What can oppose and control such apparently inevitable instabilities? Perhaps the only force strong enough and consistent enough for this purpose is the power of individual motivations. The American designers chose to use what psychologists emphasize today; the power of immediate feedback in shaping individual behavior. Hamilton said it as well as any behaviorist: "Momentary passions and immediate interests have a more active and imperious control over human conduct than general or remote considerations of policy, utility or justice."

They tried to apply to every constitutional provision a detailed examination of the personal interests of the different parties involved, showing how this official's self-interest would make him watchful of the others, and how that man's ambition would tend to make him more honest and diligent if he could run for reelection. They tried to show how the various election mechanisms and other regulations that they adopted would act to shape behavior not by mere "prohibitions on paper," which they scorned, but by shaping cooperating or conflicting personal or group interests or behavioral feedbacks.

Over and over again we see them using this kind of analysis of individual interests in studying the problems that would come up and in trying to invent solutions. Will political opposition sometimes be unreasonable? Of course. "Men often oppose a thing, merely because they have had no agency in planning it, or because it may have been planned by those whom they dislike."

How can we prevent the almost inevitable concentration of power in the hands of ambitious officials?

The great security against a gradual concentration of the several powers in the same department, consists in giving to those who administer each department the necessary constitutional means and personal motives to resist the encroachments of the others . . . Ambition must be made to counteract ambition. The interest of the man must be connected with the constitutional rights of the place. It may be a reflection on human nature that such devices should be necessary to control the abuses of government. But what is government itself but the greatest of all reflections on human nature? If men were angels, no government would be necessary.

How can minorities be protected from improper treatment by a majority? "If a majority be united by a common interest, the rights of the minority will be insecure . . . [But in the United States], the society itself will be broken into so many parts, interests, and classes of citizens, that the rights of individuals, or of the minority, will be in little danger from interested combinations of the majority."

The resemblance of the Federalist approach to the modern feedback approach is shown especially clearly by their discussion of the best time-constants the system should have for adjusting to various changes and stresses. It is a response-idea, or feedback-idea, quite different from the simpler static idea of a mechanical balance of forces or an instantaneous balance of ballots. They devote one essay (No. 70) to methods of obtaining "energy and despatch" in executive actions; three others (52, 53, and 61) to obtaining rapid responsiveness in the lower House; another (62) to obtaining in turn a protection against its "sudden and violent passions" by having an upper House with a "tenure of considerable duration"; and another (78) to obtaining long-time stability and independence in judicial interpretations of the fundamental laws.

The need for different time-constants for different purposes is discussed explicitly.

Energy in government is essential to . . . security. . . . Stability in government . . . is essential to . . . repose and confidence in the minds of the people. . . . The genius of Republican liberty, seems to demand . . . that those entrusted with [power] should be kept in dependence on the people, by a short duration of their appointments . . . Stability, on the contrary, requires that the hands, in which power is lodged, should continue for a length of time, the same.

And when they try to provide methods for changing the Constitution itself, they try to guard equally "against that extreme facility which would render the Constitution too mutable; and that extreme difficulty which might perpetuate its discovered faults."

It is now recognized that any complex system, in order to survive, must have just such a distribution of time-constants and rates of adjustment; that is, in Ross Ashby's terminology, it must have "multistability," with successive levels of stable defense against different levels and rates of stress and change. How else can a system deal with both the fast problems of a Pearl Harbor and with the slowly changing problems of women's rights or the organization of labor?

NEED FOR A MINIMUM SYSTEM

One further aspect of the Federalist approach deserves emphasis in connection with our problem of world stability today; that is, their insistence on making a system that would be adequate against the foreseeable dangers, but that would be otherwise a minimum system, with minimum interference with any other matters. Adoption of the Constitution was a touch-and-go matter anyway, requiring delicate compromises; but it would have been impossible if it had encroached any further on state sovereignty or private affairs. No provision could be included that could not be proved necessary to the success of the design. The Federalists had to emphasize that the new Constitution was the minimum possible, and that if in some cases it was a little hard to swallow, it could be changed if necessary, and in any case would soon pay off with immediate positive advantages for each state that accepted it. The authors said:

The powers proposed to be lodged in the Federal Government, are as little formidable to those reserved to the individual States, as they are indispensibly necessary to accomplish the powers of the Union. . . .

The system, though it may not be perfect in every part, is upon the whole a good one, is the best that the present views and circumstances of the country will permit. . . . I should esteem it the extreme of imprudence to prolong the precarious state of our national affairs, and to expose the union to the jeopardy of successive experiments, in the chimerical pursuit of a perfect plan. . . .

Under a vigorous national government, the natural strength and resources of the country [will be] directed to a common interest [and nothing will] restrain our growth . . . An unrestrained intercourse between the States themselves will advance the trade of each, by an interchange of their respective productions . . . The veins of com-

merce in every part will be replenished, and will acquire additional
motion and vigour from a free circulation of the commodities of
every part.

These predictions proved to be exactly correct. Is there any
better test of whether they understood the mechanisms?

The failure of Americans generally to understand these basic
principles in their own system has probably had as much as
anything to do with our inability to export our stability and
prosperity to our friends and imitators abroad. A purely legalistic concern with representation formulas or with the "separation
of powers" is not enough; nor the lip service that is paid to
"checks and balances" in many textbooks. Probably many of the
new democratic nations and groups that later adopted models of
the U.S. Constitution and found them to fail did not pay sufficient attention to these detailed feedback considerations. Probably they made changes, such as proportional representation, or
limitation on terms of office, that seem minor but that actually
tend to disorganize the structure; or perhaps they preserved
other features whose operation depends on attitudes peculiar to
the American tradition. Certainly many American state constitutions, like those whose defects are analyzed in such detail in the
Federalist papers, are superficially like the U.S. Constitution,
but omit many of the little feedbacks that tend to promote honesty, efficiency, and continuity, and so give the states today the
same reputation they had then, of tending to be more corrupt
and more inert and more unstable than the Federal system.

I am not supposing, of course, that the American founding
fathers had any monopoly on social-feedback thinking. Modern
workers, notably in the fields of monetary theory and industrial
management and to some degree in operations research and
systems theory, have gone very much further in a few problems,
in mathematically applying the idea of feedback in social networks to prediction and control.

And great progress has certainly been made in the design of
larger social organizations. For example, several countries and
groups of countries, now exhibit rationally planned and successful economic or political systems with internal stabilization mechanisms that permit free and rapid development with mutual

security against either chaos or exploitation. One thinks particularly of the European Common Market, whose dramatic unification of formerly competing nations within a few short years, is evidence of subtle control mechanisms ingeniously designed to produce mutual confidence and mutual growth in an economic chain-reaction. On the Communist side, Marx and Engels, like the Federalists, did much of their analysis on the basis of a historical examination of the behavior and tendencies of competing men and groups. The study and comparison of such efforts at social engineering in various countries, and the different control mechanisms and points of success and failure, will be most rewarding.

Are these attempts relevant to the problem of stabilizing the world today? I am sure they are. It is true that our present problem is vastly more difficult than any earlier problem, because of our three billion population and our hundred-odd multilingual countries in many stages of development. But we are also better equipped to handle it. We have new political and economic and engineering understanding, and we now have a real theory of feedback and stability. Today we might be able to design new stabilization structures that would have much more subtle, responsive, and effective feedbacks than any used in social design before. So it is not impossible that if we put our minds to it we could design structures based on this new sophistication that would increase our security and stability just as suddenly and dramatically as the U.S. Constitution did 200 years ago.

It is therefore not the analogy of the early American situation or their particular historical answers that I particularly want to emphasize. It is the analogy of their conscious attempt to design, and to get adopted, a set of stabilization mechanisms that enabled free but interacting groups to continue to live and act and be prosperous in the same world together without always threatening and fighting each other.

REQUIREMENTS FOR WORKABILITY

What would be the requirements for a peace-keeping system among a hundred sovereign states today?

If we think about this problem with the Federalist example in mind, I think we will see that there are at least four requirements for a successful solution.

The first is that it must work. That is, it must be a scheme or system actually capable of keeping the peace of the world against explosion under most of the foreseeable sources of instability for at least a generation or two. Second, it must be capable of modification as need develops and as experience develops. Third, it must nevertheless be a minimum program, making an absolute minimum of interference with the internal workings of presently established governments. And fourth, it must be a system with positive rewards, offering the nations and their present leaders, whether these are committees or dictators or elected officials, maximum advantages in domestic support, and positive reasons for wanting to adopt or join such a scheme.

To say that an acceptable system must work is to say a number of things. It means in the first place that it must contain many "checks and balances" or feedbacks, like those in the Constitution, contrived so that human feedback reactions are continually called forth from one side or the other, adequate and directive enough to dissipate or avert or correct both the deteriorative and the explosive dangers from any quarter—insolvency, coups d'état, Hitlers, or mutual escalation—before they become unmanageable.

In addition, a workable system must be tough-minded. It must assume the worst—that men are "ambitious, vindictive, and rapacious," as Hamilton said—so that it can deal with such problems not merely when they appear, but before they appear; it must therefore have these checks and balances prepared in advance. It is impossible to overestimate the importance of being a "realist" in this sense, because no system can be adopted unless it can convince the intelligent conservatives and nationalist leaders in every country that it will work, by showing them explicitly a clear sequence of steps and mechanisms for averting or dealing with any probable crisis problem or combination of them.

It goes without saying, of course, that a truly realistic system can never be based primarily on last-ditch punishment or retaliation; a constant expectation of reliance on this would destroy the feeling of security that is aimed at, as we all know today. A good working system is based rather on continuous pressures and rewards for cooperative behavior and on continuous and almost automatic dissipation of threats to peace and stability; and when it works well, as in a good scientific laboratory or on a "happy ship," threats of punishment recede into the background and the group begins to perform wonders.

Utopians and the framers of imaginary systems and constitutions have frequently concentrated on such things as spelling out sanctions or numerical representation formulas; and they have often omitted important little feedbacks; or have anticipated that goodwill and better education would enable a good world government to dispense with those checks on each other's behavior that are the hardest to specify because they are the hardest to agree on—and consequently the most necessary. This is like assuming that a good furnace will "naturally" keep the house the right temperature when the feedback thermostat has been taken away. It is true that a smoothly functioning social feedback system, like a team working together on a space flight, both requires and generates a lot of internal cooperation and goodwill. But this is not because it assumes goodwill, or because it is based on laws or charters that punish the lack of it; but because its operating rules lead to many little rewards for the little communications and checks and decisions that push steadily in the same cooperative direction.

The principal effect of laws and government organization on our collective life is not to set limits or to mete out punishment, any more than the principal effect of economics is to award profits. The principal effect of both is to tie the extreme ends of a fabric of hundreds and thousands of unnoticed little tendencies and feedbacks that continuously channel and amplify men's effort in certain directions of cooperation. These are the feedbacks that it is essential to plan and control, the ones that determine success or failure, and that are smaller but are more realistic, more steady, more irresistible and far more important than the best preambles or the most effortful goodwill.

Finally, "workability" requires that the feedbacks have various time-constants for various purposes. Some must be of a fast executive type, able to deal with surprise attack. Others must be designed to slow down certain types of changes, perhaps by forcing them to be considered at length by several deliberative bodies, so that healthy interrelationships will have time to grow and will not be disrupted by the constant fluctuation of public opinion or the threat of it.

OTHER REQUIREMENTS

Modifiability is the second requirement in a successful system for keeping the peace. In a changing world, no system could be perfect or could stay perfect for long. The best system demands, not so much a plan ideal in every detail to begin with, as a plan with provisions for being changed and adapted as imperfections appear or as conditions change. In the long run, any system that is not modifiable by feasible and orderly procedures in a reasonable time, is brittle, for it will force stresses to build up higher and higher until some part of the structure is broken, and broken suddenly and dangerously.

There are some changes in conditions, such as those in population or power, that might be handled in advance by such devices as representation formulas that allow for changes; but there must be provision also for recognition and adoption of more basic changes when unanticipated difficulties or injustices appear in the working of the system. Needless to say, the possibility of modification would make it much easier for many governments that have particular initial objections, to accept a proposed system if it offers a clear mechanism by which they can work to modify it in the direction of their needs, and if it offers a reasonable expectation of success. The need for modifiability in a reasonable time is evident in many of the "package deals" for disarmament that have been proposed by both East and West in recent years.

The third requirement for success is that the system must be an absolute minimum system. Adoption of any workable system for keeping the peace is going to be almost if not quite impossible, considering the conflicting interests and requirements of various governments and countries in various stages of development and ambition that have to be satisfied. Even with every group as aware as it can be of the catastrophic nuclear alternatives, and even with every country and leader actually making an effort to be tolerant and generous, the step to a real peace-keeping system will be the most difficult collective step that human beings have ever taken. Of course, it may prove to be impossible, if short-sightedness and opposition and despair win out; if so, the human experiment may come to a radioactive end. But if it is possible at all, every country is going to have to make a few real concessions in what it thinks are its interests, and every real leader is going to have to show his people the need and the value of such concessions. One of the hard and central concessions, for every country, is going to be giving up the demands we make on other countries and other leaders, when these demands have nothing directly to do with the peace-keeping mechanism. No refusal to communicate with de facto governments, no ideological objections, and no righteous indignation over their past actions or their present corruption or oppression, should be allowed to increase by a single degree the difficulty of obtaining adoption of such a necessary scheme.

To get any structure adopted at all, it must therefore be the minimum structure that will actually keep the peace for a reasonable time between nations. This means that it must make no interference with present internal governments or policies of any country and no interference with commercial or ideological relationships between countries, except what is absolutely necessary to the peace-keeping function. And it must provide mechanisms, as already noted, for the correction of small and large difficulties, for the satisfaction of disputes and the adjustment of pressures and even for deliberated changes in the basic structure, so as to increase the willingness of nations to accept it in spite of particular initial dissatisfactions. Likewise, the feedback controls designed to make the system stable must not be any more obvious or more obnoxious in their operation than is absolutely necessary. Except for last-ditch mechanisms, many of the arrangements will be more palatable to the parties and will work best if the feedbacks are gentle and steady, like the hope of better economic conditions; if the feedbacks are implicit and not explicit, operating not by coercion but by offering opportunities, operating simply by pushing the tendencies and interests of governments and of leaders steadily in the direction of more international stability rather than less.

In this connection, it may be important to emphasize that a

minimum, and adoptable, peace-keeping structure will *not* be a World Government. It is not a structure designed to satisfy "men of goodwill" but one to satisfy strong conservatives and patriots in every country who do not want to give up their independence of action but who finally do not want to die hard. It would have to have strictly limited powers and limited responsibilities and strictly limited interference with national governments. For simplicity and for acceptability, many world problems would have to be explicitly barred from its province, including such important questions as the legality of governments, the rights of minorities, universal education, economic development, population control, and the use of resources. Much of the information a peace-keeping corps turns up would probably have to be secret from other individuals and from other governments and from other world organizations, just as the individual information turned up by the U.S. Census and the Treasury Department is secret from other individuals and agencies of the U.S. government. At best, a peace-keeping structure might be a shield under whose protection the first steps towards more general and profitable forms of world organizations could take place with some assurance of survival. But it can only be adopted by offering to every nation for a long time to come the right to keep its own rules and its own secrets and its own insularity, whether foolish or not. One has only to consider the difficulties of adopting even a minimum peace-keeping structure to realize how far beyond us any agreement on the more controversial aspects of world organization still is.

Finally, it is worth noting that any program will be most readily adoptable if it offers immediate and clear positive rewards. That is, if it holds out not merely the negative advantage of survival, but clear positive advantages of personal and national self-interest; if the new opportunities for unhampered development at home and abroad are spelled out in personal terms; and if leaders show how to convert the reduction of armaments and taxes not into unemployment and loss of income but into increased leisure and higher personal real income. Jean Monnet did not spell out the disadvantages of tariffs, he spelled out the advantages of the European Common Market; and the thing was born. If the peace is kept, there are many real and tangible advantages of this kind that can be seized on and dramatized, so that they would help to outweigh the internal stresses produced by changes in the military and industrial structure in each country, even for conservatives and for those with a personal stake in maintaining the present system.

None of these requirements are primarily legal or diplomatic requirements. We need lawyers, but not a lawyers' Constitution. We need diplomats, but not a diplomatic impasse. We do not need a system that punishes and postures, but a working system that bargains and compromises and achieves. For a peace-keeping structure to be adopted and successful, it must be effective, modifiable, minimal, and rewarding.

STABILIZATION MECHANISMS
FOR NUCLEAR AUTHORITY

It may be worth listing a few of the more special problems of a long-run peace-keeping structure that seem to need detailed analysis of the factors making for system stability under various disturbances, and that should be argued out hardheadedly by theoretical and practical men from different countries.

One of these special problems is the nature of the nuclear authority in the world. Up to this point, I have been careful not to call the peace-keeping structure an "agency," any more than a productive economic system would be called an agency; and I have not mentioned any division of it into "executive," "legislative," and "judicial," bodies and the like, because these are some of the very points that ought to be matters of analysis before a decision is made. But clearly, somewhere in the structure, whatever its form, there must be some kind of responsibility and authority to watch over nuclear power and to control any nuclear explosives that exist or that might be produced. One of the special problems is therefore the nature of this authority. Regardless of how it is elected or appointed or perpetuated, there will be the question, should it have a central head? Should it have a single headquarters in an internationalized zone? Should it be guarded by its own troops?

Or should it have a dispersed authority, with subgroups controlling and guarding nuclear weapons dispersed in various countries? Some pressure toward unity is obviously essential, to avoid the constant possibility of divisive ambition and faction that the Federalists so emphasized, but the answers to these questions are not necessarily made simple by this rule. For example, the present great powers might be somewhat more willing to relinquish control of their present nuclear weapons, if these could be left for some years in their present physical locations, where they could be seized from an international guard in case of supposed catastrophic need. The presence of the guard to delay the seizure and to set off international warning systems might permit other countries to feel a little more secure than they do today; but it would be a "Fail-Safe" system from the point of view of the nuclear nation today, and therefore perhaps a little more acceptable to it in the beginning.

The right of every American to bear arms was regarded by the makers of the Constitution as the best protection against tyrants, and the right of every state to its own militia was regarded as the best protection against the invasions of other states or against usurpation of the federal power. These arms could be trusted not to lead to domestic convulsions, once a peace-keeping structure was set up that provided other mechanisms for reducing the fears and channeling the disagreements of the states. The right of the great states today to have their own nuclear weapons offers them the same kind of apparent protection against invasion of their rights. It is not a real protection, in view of their probable total annihilation if the weapons should ever be used, but the loss of this right and of this apparent protection that they now have is the real sticking point against disarmament proposals for conservatives in all these countries. Without trying to decide here all the questions that such thoughts raise, it is clear that no long-run peace-keeping structure is likely to be adopted, any more than the Constitution was likely to be adopted, unless it guarantees to the conservatives in all states the retention of much of the arms and the supposed protection they now have; that is, unless it offers "Fail-Safe" provisions to the interests of the great powers as well as offering "Fail-Safe" provisions to the world.

Another problem is the problem of the military organization of the peace-keeping structure. It is not absurd to suppose that there must be some peace-keeping military organization or repository of power even in a disarmed or partly disarmed world. Armies have already fought under the United Nations flag in a number of small conflicts. How to make the command of such an organization responsive to the collective interests of all, so that it would be restrained from the development of dictatorial ambition over the years, but would still be energetic and effective, was a question of central importance in the Constitution and it is one of central importance in making a stable structure today. The inadequacy of the present United Nations arrangements on this score has been obvious every time its armies have been called out.

No peace-keeping structure of any kind can survive for long unless it has built into it wise stabilizing measures to deal with several questions. How is the command elected or appointed and with what tenure? Who are the commanders accountable to? What will guarantee—in a disarmed world—that one or more of them will not ignore or even hold hostage their civilian commanders or assemblies? What guarantees that they will not act for private ambition or for their country of origin? What is to limit their possible excesses or ruthlessness and torture? And so on. A Federalist type of analysis of these potential problems, setting up checks and interlocking mechanisms to provide some measure of control in advance of contingencies, might make disarmament more palatable to men in many countries.

STABILIZATION OF REVENUE

We should also note that a third crucial problem in keeping the peace is the mechanism of obtaining revenue to support the operations of the peace-keeping structure, including its military organization, its nuclear control and disarmament-watching operations and the associated scientific and technical staffs that would be needed. The United Nations is having trouble today obtaining its assessed revenues and in selling bonds to governments to support its operations. No one could be surprised at this who had read Hamilton's description of the similar troubles of the original Confederation of the thirteen states, troubles stemming from exactly the same mistake in attempting to get revenue directly from the states themselves. If, for the words "states" and "United States," we read "nations" and "United Nations," his description in *The Federalist* fits exactly today:

The United States [under the Confederation] have an indefinite discretion to make requisitions for men and money; but they have no authority to raise either by regulations extending to the individual citizens of America. The consequence of this is, that though in theory their resolutions concerning those objects are laws, constitutionally binding on the members of the Union, yet in practice they are mere recommendations, which the States observe or disregard at their option. . . . It is evident, that there is no process of a court by which their observance of the laws can in the last resort be enforced. Sentences may be denounced against them for violations of their duty; but these sentences can only be carried into execution by the sword. . . .

The greater deficiencies of some States furnished the pretext of example and the temptation of interest to the complying, or to the least delinquent States. Why should we do more in proportion than those who are embarked with us in the same political voyage? Why should we consent to bear more than our proper share of the common burthen? These were suggestions which human selfishness could not withstand, and which even speculative men, who looked forward to remote consequences, could not, without hesitation, combat. Each State yielding to the persuasive voice of immediate interest and convenience has successively withdrawn its support, 'till the frail and tottering edifice seems ready to fall upon our heads and to crush us beneath its ruins.

Is this not the essential problem of the United Nations now? What is the remedy? Several avenues need to be explored which will relieve a peace-keeping organization from this kind of financial dependence on the goodwill and support of separate governments. One possibility today might be a tax on individual incomes all over the world, but this would obviously be attended by the greatest difficulties of collection as well as by the generation of extensive individual resentment. A simpler and more promising method might be the imposition of a small tax, of perhaps one-tenth or two-tenths of one per cent, on international trade—which was what the Federalists concluded they should try. Trade is an operation that stands to benefit most by the maintenance of peace, where the taxation would not be burdensome and would not require repeated appeals to legislatures and governments; and it flows through a small enough number of channels between nations that the revenue might be monitored and collected with comparative ease.

Another important problem to be settled for a peace-keeping organization would be the basis of national representation in it when decisions need to be made or disputes need to be adjudicated. Today the United Nations has a double structure between the General Assembly and the Security Council, but no one would claim that this reflects either the populations of the world or the power of the world with any accuracy. What flexible interrelation of representations would keep the peace more successfully over the long run, insuring that the grievances of various populations do not slip beyond representation and correction and that the changing realities of technical power do not slip beyond control? Should there be representation based on population? On nuclear force? On gross national product? Even with the best of disarmament schemes, our failure to have a system that adjusts its representation and control to keep up with the present human and technical explosions could lead to unchecked resentment and bloody war within less than a generation.

And one further problem that obviously deserves the attention of social engineers today is the optimal distribution of time-constants for assessing problems and making changes and carrying out different functions in a peace-keeping structure. Like the structure set up by the U.S. Constitution, any peace-keeping organization needs to combine responsiveness with stability. It might need to have a reaction time measured in hours or minutes for coping with insurgent seizures of nuclear weapons, while it might need a time-constant of years for evaluating defects in its organizational structure.

Likewise in holding office, the rates of turnover and mixtures of rates in various jobs will strongly affect the preparation, skill, breadth, boredom, complacency, collusion, and anxiety of the men who hold them. The effects will be different on men from different cultural backgrounds. Different time-constants and mechanisms for appointments and for critical review and promotion will be needed for different kinds of positions in the army, in scientific laboratories, in management positions, and in elective offices. The energy and honesty and efficiency of the whole system may depend crucially on making optimum choices and assignments in these matters. This is obvious to any feedback engineer, but is often not adequately considered by the makers of Constitutions.

WHAT MUST BE DONE

It is clear that all these questions are hard; but not nearly so hard as some suppose. It is most important and hopeful to realize that doing serious and wise feedback thinking on these various questions is not a matter demanding whole scholarly life-times, but might be only a matter of a few short months. It is not a matter of great congresses of men, at least in working out the basic principles of design, but a matter of getting together a few clear and practical thinkers. The Constitution was hammered out in four months by less than forty delegates, and *The Federalist* papers were written in another seven months by three men. Probably the basic feedback rules of the European Common Market were devised and agreed upon in a similarly short number of sessions.

The stabilization-design problem does not need to arouse so many antagonisms as the direct-confrontation disarmament problem which has dragged on with its stalemated meetings for years. A workable and adoptable system of rules, commitments, and authority, limited specifically to the problem of keeping the peace in a partly disarmed world, might be worked out as well as it could be worked out, in no more than a few months of dedicated study by a few practical men from different countries who understand these principles. It is obviously urgent for the world to try to bring such a group of men together, with such an assignment, for this length of time.

The possibility of adoption afterwards would depend critically, of course, on what kind of men they are. In order to be sure that they consider realistically the important contingencies and their effect on human and national behavior, they would need to be men experienced in different kinds of governments and in the failures and successes of various government planning schemes and international control mechanisms in the last few years. They would need to be informed or able to inform themselves on nuclear control and detection problems, as well as on developments in other ultimate weapons or pacifying devices. They would need to be solid and influential men, respected by a majority of citizens in their own countries as well as by the governments in power, so that their endorsement of any peace-keeping program would find a following, and would be regarded as hardheaded and workable and as an improvement in their national security rather than a "sell-out to the enemy." They would need to be trusted enough to be allowed to discuss alternatives and consequences in private meetings without having to follow a rigid line laid down by their home governments, because only in this way would they have a chance of devising peace-keeping structures that would be stable regardless of future upsets and changes in governments.

There are such men in every country. They are precisely the men who might be most willing to be "realists" in admitting each other's existence and each other's objectives and each other's weapons, and who might be most willing to try to make a very limited and politically neutral peace-keeping structure.

The realization that such a structure, wise and workable, might be formed out of a small study conference of such men; the realization that it would bring immediate positive rewards in prosperity and consumer goods to nearly every country, enough to counterbalance the loss of military jobs, because of the increase in commercial and consumer confidence and the expansion of trade; and the realization that many different national objections as well as national objectives can be accommodated, if an absolute minimum program is what is aimed at; all these suggest that the formation of a hard-headed peace-keeping structure is not as hopeless as has been supposed.

ESSENTIALS AND NON-ESSENTIALS

For it has never been emphasized and sufficiently appreciated that there is not just one, but many peace-keeping systems that will work. Once the essential feedbacks have been provided for, there is latitude in all other matters for realistic compromises among the parties. This is what permits such a system to be actually adoptable and workable, and this is why Madison sneered at theoretical rigidity, at "that artificial structure and regular symmetry, which an abstract view of the subject might lead an ingenious theorist to bestow on a Constitution planned in his closet or in his imagination." In stabilizing feedback systems, a wide latitude of variation is always possible, provided certain small fundamentals are observed. A stabilized biological system, for instance, such as an animal or other organism which has multiple feedbacks to maintain its many vital forms and interrelate them properly, may take many forms. A successful industrial organization, which is stabilized by numerous internal communications and feedbacks, may take many forms. Likewise, there are very many variant arrangements that will keep the peace, just as there are very many variant arrangements that will destroy it. If any workable arrangement can be adopted to start with, it may well evolve into different and better forms over the years, once it begins to be past the immediate danger of destroying us all.

But those few small fundamentals—feedback fundamentals—do have to be observed. If a league of states continues to try to collect its funds from the separate states, it will break up into debt and helplessness and chaos no matter what variations it tries. But if it collects more subtly and directly from multiple commercial channels or from millions of individuals, there are a hundred variant schemes it can use that will not interfere with its prosperity and growth. Likewise, as we saw earlier, the proportional-representation system of elections, in most of its variant forms, leads office-seekers to make strategic choices that always tend to split the electorate into small blocs and factions and to make government unstable. But majority elections, under many different districting arrangements, tend to press the electorate into two or three large pluralistic and more representative parties. These are elementary feedback rules of social engineering, some of them known for two hundred years, but many professors of economic and political science do not know them, and the men who framed the unstable constitutions of some modern European countries did not know them, nor the men who framed that of the United Nations. Once such feedback rules are understood and used as the Federalists used them, men can frame a peace-keeping structure which will accommodate a large range of national requirements and circumstances, but which will nevertheless give us all a greatly increased measure of safety and confidence and hope for our own future and the future of man.

When men need to build a new building, they call in architects. Calling together a conference of architects who can design a better, safer structure for the world is now our only hope and our most urgent and inescapable need if we are to survive even another decade without probable catastrophe.

The solution of social problems lags behind technology because we have not organized the same sharp search for ideas to deal with them.

Research and Development for Social Problems

Where can seed operations and other mechanisms for directing and modifying social change be initiated? In many places, of course. Yet when we think about it we see that our society has not yet developed any very systematic method for dealing with this problem, even though this is a time of the most rapid and upsetting changes, when the wise design and shaping of our changes is a matter of absolutely vital importance to human happiness and the survival of ourselves and our children.

We have many organizations searching all the time for new inventions and combinations of them to solve technical problems. The research and development teams of our industrial and government laboratories do nothing else. Within a few years their new technology changes our social structure and all our ways of living and working.

But we have no corresponding organizations that spend all their time searching deliberately in this way for new inventions and combinations for the solution of social problems. There is no General Electric, no national laboratory with full-time research and development teams assigned to come up with ingenious ideas of improved social organization and communication and interaction, and to set them in motion. A good many industrial managers may be on the lookout for continual improvements in their own organizations, making use of everything from operations research groups to employee suggestion boxes. A league for political action may work hard to get particular improvements adopted on the local or national political scene. Sometimes a self-appointed university or foundation group may search for new ways of dealing with a particular problem. But where is there any large corporation trying systematically to produce better ideas for better living in our local and national social and political structures, or in the malfunctioning public sector of the economy, or in the problems of conflict, ignorance, and want that our improved technology leaves untouched? The main reason why our solution of social problems lags so far behind our magnificent technology today may be that we have not yet organized the same deliberate search for ideas to deal with them.

Yet "social inventions" are possible, as we have seen, just as possible as technological ones, and might be searched for in the same way. Think of those social inventions like the alphabet, the business corporation, standard time, the credit card, or the research-and-development team (supposed to have been introduced first by Edison). These things are all like technological inventions in that they were "problem-oriented" ideas, undoubtedly invented specifically to solve particular problems after these problems had become clear. Some of them were originally devised for personal profit, some not. But they are again like successful technological inventions, in that they were "self-propagating" after the initial step, because they were so clearly profitable for the users that they were taken up and imitated rapidly in a kind of chain-reaction that produced great social consequences.

Almost anyone will be able to think of dozens of such social inventions. It is instructive to look at a few recent ones, including some we have already touched on in this book, just to see under what conditions they are now being produced and whether it might be possible to generate them more systematically. I would mention three which date from the years 1942–1954:

The pay-as-you-go income tax, resulting from the efforts of one man, Beardsley Ruml.

The accelerated search for oral contraceptives, partly the result of efforts by Leo Szilard and Harrison Brown.

The international nuclear test-ban proposal, which seems to have been first put forward publicly in an article in the *Bulletin of the Atomic Scientists* in 1954 by David Inglis of the Argonne National Laboratory.

All these ideas had major social consequences within two to ten years after their initial proposal—that is, in a time which is shorter than the time for many technical inventions to become effective on a large scale. The pay-as-you-go law increased the scale of government operations; the oral contraceptives have made the world population problem seem manageable for the first time; and the nuclear test-ban has grown in ten years to a ratified treaty and a hopeful factor in international life.

Of course these thumbnail summaries do not do justice to all the other men who had similar ideas at about the same time, or who contributed to the realization of these ideas in the later stages, when the commitment and courage of a few sometimes made the difference between success and failure. But they will suffice to illustrate several points about the genesis of modern social inventions.

First, these particular inventions are problem-oriented in their origins. Second, they are not technical ideas (although the oral contraceptive example revolves around a central technical problem) ; they are social-organizational ideas. Third, we see that they appear and are taken up sporadically and in diverse ways at present. They frequently come to birth without the knowledge or support of administrations or official groups, just as individual technical inventions came to birth in the nineteenth century before we had regular research-and-development teams.

But finally, and most importantly, we see that the atmosphere of university discussions, "looking forward and backward and in all directions," appears to be a fertile place for generating such ideas. Two of these inventions were devised in the context of an academic group that had decided to examine a particular problem, looking explicitly for effective ideas of this type. Szilard and Brown's efforts were the outcome of a regular series of discussions organized after the war among a small group of physicists, chemists, and biologists to look into the question of what were the most serious future problems of mankind and what could be done about them. After a number of technical studies (see Harrison Brown's book, *The Challenge of Man's Future*) they concluded that the population explosion would be the great danger, and that stepping up the search for a cheap and effective oral contraceptive was the best way to avert it. Inglis' proposal seems to have been a more individual idea, but at least it arose in the context of the meetings of the local university chapter of the Federation of American Scientists, which was debating, after the first hydrogen bombs had been exploded, what practical steps might actually be adopted that would reduce the danger of nuclear escalation.

It could be a major contribution to ameliorating the problems of the city, the nation, and the world, if universities could set up specific task forces of this kind—social research-and-development teams—made up of thinkers and ingenious minds from several different disciplines, to look for other useful new social inventions in particular areas and to set them in motion. These problems are too far-reaching and too practical to be attacked within ordinary academic departments. But the university as a whole is probably the best place—perhaps the only possible place —for this kind of search, because of its stores of information on every subject, its collection of diverse talents and specialties, its detachment, and its increasing role as the center of seminal ideas, technical and social, for our whole society. The research and development for the new technology has depended heavily on the general knowledge and the basic research discoveries in the laboratories of the universities and great technical institutes; but the schools may have an even more important role to play in the kind of social research and development outlined here, because they are the only institutions in our society that can do the job.

There are many problems today that could be studied profitably with such an approach. Society is at least as intricate as an automobile, and the number of new social inventions we could use may well be comparable to the total number of General Motors patents. In several areas, the rewards for study by a university task force might be especially dramatic.

1. New methods of financial support for the United Nations, methods which do not involve repeated annual exposure to

legislative or governmental veto by separate states. In the last chapter we discussed the theoretical and historical evidence and the early warnings about the instability of this method of obtaining revenue. Perhaps it would be impossible at this stage for the United Nations to obtain its support generally from individual citizens rather than from governments. But if it could begin to do so in a few major countries (perhaps offering something like individual voting rights on certain issues in exchange for the small taxation), this might provide a firmer basis for its long-range operations, and might have advantages that would persuade additional countries to come around to this method of support. A second alternative that might deserve consideration, as we saw, is the possibility of obtaining some basic United Nations support from a tax of, say, a few tenths of one per cent on international trade. Such a tax could be essentially automatic in its operation, and could be monitored and collected at relatively few ports of entry; and it would particularly affect just those operations that stand to benefit most greatly from a strengthened and stabilized United Nations. Obtaining support through a small tax on other international operations such as, for example, a tax on world communications satellites, or leases on ocean mining rights, would have similar advantages.

2. Improvements in methods and devices for speeding up language teaching. English is spreading at the rate of, let us say, 100 million additional speakers every year. But if the world population also grows by 100 million a year, there is little net gain. Could the spread of this *lingua franca* not be greatly accelerated with the help of new ideas? The time it takes now to get a working knowledge of a foreign language is said to be about twelve weeks of intensive study. Could it be cut to six weeks? Or to three?—perhaps by using some of the new "instant-reinforcement" methods of the psychologists? Could our rather clumsy language tapes or television teaching devices be greatly simplified or adapted for easier use in poor countries? New phonetic alphabets are now used in some kindergartens—would they facilitate the learning of English for adults as they seem to do for children? A mere 30 per cent speed-up in language learning time might double the number of new speakers added to the English-speaking world every year, and might make all the differ-

ence in the eventual orientation and attitudes of the underdeveloped countries and their ease of intercommunication and their
speed of utilization of our advanced technology.

3. New methods of teaching in the age-range from one to
five. A number of lines of evidence now suggest that a child's
intellectual abilities and social outlook may not be inborn so
much as learned in the earliest years. Would a new kind of
teaching study for this age-range, using all our new knowledge
of learning processes and of the development and adaptation of
the human brain, show us how to produce a great increase in the
number of exceptional minds among our children?

4. New and easier methods of organizing, recording, and dis-
tributing scholarly and technical knowledge. Many groups are
studying this problem in one context or another, for example,
from the point of view of library design, or that of information
classification and access, or that of publication, storage, and reproduction, but few of these groups see the problem from the
point of view of the whole spread of human knowledge and its
increased access for society as a whole. A university that could
design some new social inventions to facilitate and upgrade the
communications, information, and knowledge-handling of the
whole community might find itself multiplying its services to the
community and the nation many times over.

5. Physical analysis of what might be called "Gresham's law
areas" in modern society, where the collective behavior and pressures of separately acting individuals produce results that no
single one of them would have rationally preferred. These include semi-technical problems like traffic jams, and social problems like the real estate pressures that block rational solutions
of housing problems and produce slums, or the competitive pressures that degrade the quality of the radio and newspapers, or
that force editors and congressmen and political parties and
nations to take extreme positions, difficult to change. Such collective behavior by atoms and molecules is familiar to physicists
and chemists, and they are sometimes able to introduce small external forces that break up this collective activity in their crystals
and solutions. Is it possible that this kind of thinking would be
useful in these social problems? Traffic engineers and "queueing
theorists" have already learned a lot about how to avoid traffic

jams; could they help? There was once a similar Gresham's law
monotony in phonograph records, but it was broken when small
technical changes made possible the cheap and durable long-
playing records; is there some similar technical change that would
produce similar changes in the variety and quality of our newspapers?

Everyone will want to make up his own list of important
problems where similar glimmerings of solutions seem to deserve
study. Very likely in the long run it would be possible to build
up a fund of instances and general principles which could be
used over and over again in social engineering problems of this
kind, and which would make such studies even more effective.
It is important not to assume a static context in such thinking.
As we have seen, the whole U.S. Constitution represented the social engineering of a similar task force that in only a few months
of work was able to combine ideas in a complex design that
rapidly brought prosperity and order out of chaos. Many of our
most serious difficulties of political relationships today are only
small and corrective problems by comparison with theirs, and
might yield surprisingly easily to a similar approach. Our society has been shaped and can be shaped again by the thinking
mind, and is not doomed to everlasting tension and despair.

It might be feared that these restructuring activities would
arouse opposition from political groups, but I do not think this
is as serious a problem as some might suppose. It is the nature
of most of the inventions I have described that they—like the
Constitution—are acceptable precisely because they have been
designed to be of considerable value to all parties and consequently bypass the traditional grounds of political debate. Their
success becomes possible just because they are *not* primarily
political; and this is surely a necessary precondition for the success of future inventions of this sort.

The universities are not merely storage places for the brains
of society; they can be and are the initiating and acting centers.
The faster they grow up to assume this role, not merely in science
and technology but in all the other fields of needed biological
and social inventions, the sooner will some of our worst mal-
functions begin to be corrected.

To Be and Become

*Showing that the privacy and indeterminacy and potentiality
of man stand outside the classical, objective predictions of
science.*

Man and the Indeterminacies

Understanding the external world is the objective of science, and accurate prediction is the test of it. If we really understand genetics, we can breed better hybrid corn. If we really understand geology, we can locate minerals and oil. If we really understand the motion of the atmosphere and its water vapor, we can predict the weather.

But some of the most thought-provoking problems of science are those involving "indeterminacy," where accurate prediction for some reason becomes impossible. It is as though a sign said, "Nonsense!—Your prying or your prediction at this point interferes with itself, so your supposed observations or predictions can no longer be made objectively or meaningfully."

Many of these problems are a little bit like my answer to your question of whether I will wear my red tie tomorrow morning. I may tell you that I will. But this is an intention, not an objective prediction like predicting rain—and you will immediately show that you know this by laughing at me if I try to bet with you on it. It is obvious that my knowledge of the prediction and of the bet would change my performance, and I am likely to wear the red tie or not, as the case may be, just so I will win— or to do the converse, just to prove my unpredictability. Everyone knows, really, that predictions of one's own conscious decisions are not objective predictions in any scientific sense.

The most famous case of indeterminacy, where getting data for a prediction interacts with the outcome in somewhat the same way, is that of the Heisenberg "uncertainty principle" in atomic physics, which upset the whole philosophical world 40 years ago. But indeterminacy and related questions of prediction also touch many other problems in areas such as, for example, biology and psychology. It is interesting to look at some of these problems to see just what goes wrong with deterministic predictions and why. This gives us a much clearer view of what questions objective science can meaningfully ask and what it cannot, and what parts of life must be left out of the scientific equation. It appears that several nonclassical conclusions may be of central importance in understanding the relations between man and man and between man and the universe.

THE AREAS OF DETERMINISM

The concept of determinism is closely bound up with the concept of the "isolated system." An isolated system, in astronomy or physics or chemistry, is a body or collection of bodies—for example, the sun and planets, or the chemicals in a flask—which are supposed to interact in some respect only with each other. It is a system which an observer can either start off or can observe accurately at some initial time, and which can then continue to be observed indefinitely without any appreciable disturbance to its motions or behavior from interactions with the observer himself or with the rest of the universe. These conditions are evidently essential in order for determinism to hold, that is, in order for our specification of the initial state of the system to suffice for determining its final state accurately at any later time.

Of course, isolation from the surroundings is never perfect. The chemicals in the flask boil off into the air. The earth's tides slow down the moon by amounts that can be measured. Nevertheless, the "isolated system" is a useful and accurate approximation for most of the problems we know how to solve in physics, chemistry, and engineering; in fact, that is why we know how to solve them. If we correct for the small disturbances, Newton's laws will predict eclipses and the motions of planets or man-made satellites for years or centuries ahead. The planets are heavy bodies, not much affected by the dust in their paths or the sunbeams by which we observe them.

Few other predictions in science are as certain as those of the planets, but in most cases the uncertainties are not believed to be due to any breakdown of determinism. Forecasting the weather, for example, is difficult apparently because of the great complexity of the problem rather than because of any fundamental unpredictability. It appears that the basic equations of motion of our atmosphere are now known and that within a few years, with more extensive data collection and faster computers, fairly accurate weather forecasts will become possible for days or weeks ahead.

It was gambling that brought to physics and mathematics the first real problems in unpredictability. As early as 1650, Pascal developed the theory of probability to account for and predict the statistical odds in dice, cards, and roulette. But here again the unpredictability of a double six, although of the greatest reality to the dice player, is not regarded as true indeterminacy by the physicist. The physicist believes that the galloping cubes and the clicking wheel obey the laws of mechanics quite accurately, and that a high-speed movie camera coupled to an electronic computer could, in principle, predict at the start of the roll what numbers would turn up at the end.

Laplace, one of the giants of planetary prediction, thought that all physical problems would be like this, that the smallest particles of terrestrial matter should be, in principle, as deterministic and predictable as planets, if we found out their laws of attraction and motion. His famous statement of 1820 says:

An intelligence knowing all the forces acting in nature at a given instant, as well as the momentary positions of all things in the universe, would be able to comprehend in one single formula the motions of the largest bodies as well as of the lightest atoms in the world, provided that its intellect were sufficiently powerful to subject all data to analysis; to it nothing would be uncertain, the future as well as the past would be present to its eyes.

And he added, with Napoleonic assurance,

[Recent] discoveries . . . have brought the mind within reach of comprehending in the same analytical formula the past and the future state of the system of the world. All the mind's efforts in the search for truth tend to approximate to the intelligence we have just imagined, although it will forever remain infinitely remote from such an intelligence.

This statement is perhaps the high-water mark of the belief in the possibilities of mechanical prediction. What an extrapolation it was! It is easy to see planets, but how can we see atoms? It did not occur to Laplace to ask whether or with what wavelengths the "momentary positions of the lightest atoms" could be observed, or how they could be discriminated, or what kind of microscopes would be used and how *their* lightest atoms would be observed. Yet now in retrospect we see that these questions about how to do the operations are what make his great assertion absurd, even in principle. Laplace misled an age by supposing that physics could treat the whole universe as a simple extension of his planetary "isolated systems."

DEMONS AND DISTURBANCES

It is now clear that the isolated-system approximation runs into difficulties when it is extrapolated to atomic or cosmic or complex or subjective domains where either the initial non-interfering observation or specification of the state of the system becomes impossible in principle, or where the system cannot be regarded as isolated because of its strong interactions with the rest of the world.

In physics, these difficulties with isolation have now shown up in two famous problems, that of the "Maxwell Demon" and that of the Heisenberg "principle of indeterminacy" or "uncertainty principle." Maxwell invented his Demon in the 1860's as a whimsical illustration of an apparent paradox in thermodynamics. The Demon—or his human counterpart with a remarkably powerful microscope and a fast eye—was supposed to be able to watch the gas molecules moving toward a hole in a partition, and to let fast or "hot" molecules pass through the hole while slow or "cold" molecules were turned back. This would permit the gas on one side of the partition to get hotter and hotter, and that on the other side to get colder and colder, without any expenditure of energy—and yet such a result is against all the other well-established empirical and theoretical laws of thermodynamics.

This paradox has fascinated physicists for a hundred years. Obviously something is wrong in principle with such a Demon, but what? In 1927, Szilard finally showed that the trouble was that the Demon would simply not be able to "see" the individual hot and cold molecules against the fluctuating background of the gas. And that if he tried to see them better, say by shining a flashlight on them, then the light itself would interact with the molecules and would put in just enough disturbance of their speeds to spoil the discrimination between them. This paper of Szilard's is now recognized as the first paper in "information theory," showing that the very act of obtaining any physical information necessarily costs something in increasing the atomic disorder or "entropy," and in decreasing the deterministic predictability of the system being studied.

The Heisenberg uncertainty principle, which was also announced in 1927, says somewhat the same thing about a different problem. It asserts that the more accurately you try to observe the position of an atom or particle such as an electron, the more the light rays you use will disturb its velocity, and vice versa, so that you cannot make any deterministic statements, but only probability statements, about its future motion. Einstein intensely disliked this conclusion. He said, "The Lord God does not play dice!"; and he tried to set up one counterexample after another, in a famous correspondence with Bohr. But all of his counterexamples were refuted, and in spite of a small group of physicists today who say that there may be more certainty "behind" the uncertainty than is generally recognized, it appears that the uncertainty principle is here to stay in physics and philosophy.

To the layman, these examples may seem like atomic trivia, in spite of their fundamental importance. But there are some non-atomic problems where the inability to isolate the system being studied has led to very practical difficulties. This occurs, for example, in the analysis of "flow systems" like those we see in a waterfall, or a fire, or a biological organism. Whatever boundary you try to place around a living cell—or an elephant—food and excretions and air and water and energy and information must go in and out across that boundary, and the classical thermodynamic equations for the approach to equilibrium in isolated systems become irrelevant.

A living creature is not a sealed box. It is a flow system, and consequently it generates internal structures and concentration differences, and maintains electrical potentials that have repeatedly surprised chemists and theorists whose thermodynamic education was limited to the dogmas of molecules in a closed cylinder.

Biology may be the home of many such surprises. Its creatures are making transactions with the universe that are hard to define within bounds or to explore fully. And while these are not really problems in determinism, it still appears that many new concepts and new approximations may be needed to replace our traditional isolated-system ideas before some of these strange flow phenomena of life can be predicted accurately.

A fourth domain where the inability to isolate the system leads to difficulties is the domain of self-prediction—as in the problem of predicting which tie I will wear. The question of determinism simply ceases to be meaningful when, as in this case, there is no distinction between the predictor and the predicted system, between you as the observer or bettor and you as the observed or betted-on. This is, of course, the difficulty with introspection, and the reason why self-analysis foolishly done may destroy a man. As the quantum-mechanics people say, "Observations on your own mind are *not data* in the scientific sense . . . It is impossible for an observer to 'determine his own wavefunction'." Not everyone who studies the mind realizes this. Self-prediction has no clear deterministic meaning except for activities that begin to be outside our conscious control, such as habitual, unconscious, or reflex acts, or physiological phenomena such as the heartbeat or bleeding.

Self-predictions for groups often have little more meaning than for individuals, because again they often interact strongly with the behavior predicted. Self-fulfilling advertising or political announcements such as "Most of us want X" or "Business is getting better," as well as self-correcting warnings such as "You'll all get caught!", are deliberately intended to interact with the outcome—as we all know! There is nothing wrong with such statements; they may be extremely useful for persuasion and performance; but obviously no sensible person mistakes them for objective non-interfering predictions, any more than the self-prediction of red-tie-wearing.

INDETERMINACIES OF THE BRAIN

These familiar cases of non-isolation and indeterminacy have been much discussed, but they cease to be very profound once the principle is understood. Nevertheless, I think they give us a background for looking at three newer and more far-reaching paradoxes in the scientific study of man that deserve examination in some detail.

The first two of these paradoxes are concerned with two fundamental aspects of perception and the brain, which I like to call "privacy-indeterminacy" and "complexity-indeterminacy." Privacy-indeterminacy is the result of the fact that the nervous system greatly amplifies the tiny light signals or other signals that it detects. It now appears that a single elementary quantum of light absorbed by the eye is enough to be amplified into a sizable little electrical signal that goes through the optic nerve to the brain. But such a light quantum cannot be divided; no other eye can see the same light quantum. Even if the eye requires several of these quanta at the same time to reassure itself that it is seeing a real signal and not just some aberration of the nerves, there is still no necessary reason why these quanta—or at any rate the last and crucial one for detection—should not be entirely private to itself.

The result is that it is not possible for you to know independently whether a particular quantum has been absorbed in my eye. You cannot "determine the initial state of the system," so you cannot predict accurately whether I will see and respond to a weak light signal or not. Every elementary amplifier, whether biological or electronic, has this kind of privacy-indeterminacy. It may be built so as to work reliably and deterministically in all its parts, far above any atomic-uncertainty level, and it may be essentially free from "noise" or random behavior, but its least input is always private, so that it is paradoxically impossible to prove that any particular output pulse or signal is or is not fixed deterministically by an input. If you report seeing a bright red warning light, I may be able to confirm it, because it will send its quanta to my eyes too. But if you think you see a dim red flash and you press the button that fires the missile, my only connection to that part of the universe may be through your behavior, and I may never be able to establish whether you really saw the light or only a hallucination.

"Complexity-indeterminacy" involves a second type of non-observability in the nervous system. It is connected with the difficulty that one brain has in discovering whether another brain of equal complexity is acting deterministically or not. The trouble is that one brain does not have enough sensory cells to "determine the initial state" of all the neurons or interconnections in the other brain. This is probably a difficulty in fundamental principle, because the number of interconnections needed to make sense of the external world is probably necessarily greater than the number of sensory cells that are interconnected. For example, if we have four photocells—or four eye-spots in a primitive animal—there are 16 on-off combinations of signals from them, and it probably takes many more than four interconnections to distinguish these. In a human being, there seem to be of the order of 10^9 sensory cells in the eye and ear and other receptors, but there are some 10^{11} neurons—that is, a hundred times as many—interconnecting them in the brain.

The result is that I do not have nearly enough sensory cells to determine the state of every neuron in your brain at any given instant, even if I had enough microscopes and could use all my sensory cells for this purpose or could distinguish their 10^9 separate reports. Simply to state the problem explicitly in this way is to see how fantastically absurd the supposition is. Evidently even if I should believe and prove that any groups of neurons I study in your nervous system are completely deterministic in their behavior, I am faced with the paradox that I will not be able to make enough observations fast enough to prove that your whole brain acts this way. Thus I can never find out whether your responses at any later instant are completely determined from your initial conditions and your sensory inputs or not. It appears that the totality of your interconnections is unobservable and the totality of your behavior unpredictable by any other human being, except statistically.

We suddenly realize that our ideas of determinism have been developed on simpler problems, where the physicist or chemist with his huge 10^{11} brain and his 10^9 sensory elements, observes and relates a very much smaller number of external variables, perhaps only 100 or 1,000 or 10,000 planetary coordinates or chemical properties; and these ideas cease to be applicable when he is trying to observe something of the same order of complexity as the observer himself.

Perhaps we may be able to check up on determinism in the brains of animals with much simpler networks, such as earthworms or jellyfish, but I think that any real attempt to get around this theorem for a big mammalian brain is immediately seen to be an impossible joke. Should we try putting a human brain in a deep-freeze, and spend a few years to examine the initial state of all its 10^{11} neurons before letting them warm up so they could operate again? It turns out that this would mean measuring and recording the data at the rate of 2,000 neurons every minute, 24 hours a day, for a hundred years, before the experiment would be ready to be performed! Or if you are in more of a hurry, perhaps you might imagine using all the machine shops in the world to build 10^9 microscopes to look at the 10^{11} neurons in a single brain simultaneously. Presumably you would then train all the 10^9 adults in the world to line up the microscopes—standing in a crowd extending a mile in every direction—letting each person look at the 100 neurons he is assigned, and reporting the results simultaneously to a fantastic storage and computer system!

Somehow I think it won't work. All such attempts at evasion of the theorem are operationally absurd as applied to real live human beings in real time. Hundred-variable determinism ceases to be relevant to billion-variable systems. Even psychologists rarely stop to realize how fantastically complex we are, beyond imagining; and how private this makes us, and will always make us, to each other.

COMPLEXITY AND CHOICE

It used to be supposed by wishful philosophers that the Heisenberg indeterminacy principle was a chink in the deterministic armor of science big enough to let in "free will." This was never a very satisfactory conclusion. It meant that a man's choices, to the extent that they were not determined by his material heredity and conditioning and environment, were also not determined by any consistent sense of values or responsibility, but only by the random jumping of electrons in his nervous system. His material signals were not to be supplemented by spiritual signals but only by the noisy uncertainties of an atomic roulette wheel.

I think that privacy-indeterminacy and complexity-indeterminacy give us a much more satisfactory solution to this problem. They make it possible for a man to respond to subtle cues, to be consistent, to develop standards and objectives out of his own private experience and insight, to *choose*, in ways that can never be entirely predicted or determined by other men from their knowledge or manipulation of his material surroundings or even from the most elaborate examination of his brain.

Of course, even this assurance is not relevant to the real issue in the problem of "free will" and "determinism." It is still treating the man we are studying—or his brain—as an *object* of study, that is, as another isolated system. The real freedom of the will that is of concern in religion and voting and love is a matter of your freedom and mine to choose, from the inside, what we do. It has nothing to do with some possible evasion of determinacy in some object being studied, even if it is the brain of another choosing scientist. Free will is on this side of the barrier between observer and object; determinism or indeterminism is on the other side.

Today many are brought up unaware of this fundamental distinction. We are still under the Laplacian spell, and we think vaguely that our knowledge and wishes and actions are also things that ought to be fitted into equations sometime. But none of the equations of the objective world, no matter how great their determinism or indeterminism, can change my relationship to or my responsibility for my own choices and acts. None of the findings of the most elaborately developed biological or mental sciences will ever be able to displace the personal existential necessity: to choose, to act, so that one may be.

We begin to realize that our brains are the most complex and self-determining things in the known universe. After all the measurements of atoms and galaxies are folded into laws in some corner of our networks, there will still be universes of interrelationships in the rest of our networks to be discovered. If this property of complexity could somehow be transformed into visible brightness so that it would stand forth more clearly to our senses, the biological world would become a walking field of light compared to the physical world. The sun with its great eruptions would fade to a pale simplicity compared to a rosebush. An earthworm would be a beacon, a dog would be a city of light, and human beings would stand out like blazing suns of complexity, flashing bursts of meaning to each other through the dull night of the physical world between. We would hurt each other's eyes. Look at the haloed heads of your rare and complex companions. Is it not so?

EVOLUTION AND THERMODYNAMICS

A third paradox of man, where the early conclusions of isolated-system studies have misled us, is the paradox of evolution. From the classical physicist's point of view, evolution simply shouldn't be. Thermodynamics tells us that an isolated boxful of gas molecules will soon come to uniformity and will then persist like that indefinitely, except for small random fluctuations. Where is evolution in this? Nowhere.

But what if the box of gas is five or ten light-years on a side— say, as big as the space from here to the nearest star? We know the answer to that, regardless of classical thermodynamics, and it is far more interesting. It is our own story, the story of the collapsing of the gas to form a sun and planets, and then of the origin of life, as physicists and chemists and astronomers are now coming to believe. The isolated little box ceases to have isolated interactions or boundaries; it becomes totality. "Soon" ceases to be soon, and becomes a cosmic lifetime of perhaps billions of years. The simple collisions of the molecules cease to be simple and become involved in cosmic gravitational and magnetic fields and nuclear energy—and organic evolution.

Evidently there is something new here, some "large-scale non-classical behavior" that is not given by the small-system laws. It is not indeterminism this time, but something more like a new determinism; not a contradiction of the old laws, but an addition. In our enormous box, the old classical entropy and disorder steadily increase throughout the process, just as the Second Law says. The original energy is turned into heat and light that steadily radiates away into space, as predicted. But, in addition, something happens that is not obtained from the First or the Second or the Third Law of thermodynamics. A film of order, of life, builds up; and it now appears that this process may be just as inevitable in the flowing radiation field as the Second Law. Out of the growing and radiating disorder comes order. "Life feeds on neg-entropy," as Schrödinger put it in his little book *What Is Life?* in 1944.

The old isolated-system reasoning has failed us again by having been extrapolated from the small scale to the cosmic scale as though no new Laws could come in. Something else is needed to complete the scientific picture, a small new Fourth Law, a little bit of nonclassical behavior: the evolution of life and intelligent organisms. Perhaps from the sun's point of view, a trivial fluctuation, but to us as the intelligent organisms, a Law of some consequence.

The problem may be illuminated by an exchange I once observed between three laboratory scientists who got into a half-whimsical philosophical discussion about the I.Q. of God. I will only be exaggerating their characteristics a little if I call them a Jew, an atheist, and a Hungarian (not all the same man!). The Jew said, "God must be very intelligent because he has created all these wonderful things—DNA molecules and fish and professors." The atheist said, "Nonsense. God is very stupid. In the first place, it has taken him six billion years. And in the second place, he has done it by the clumsiest possible method, natural selection, just throwing away everything he couldn't use."

The Hungarian said, "Gentlemen, gentlemen! You don't understand your own question. What I.Q. stands for is Intelligence Quotient. And a quotient is the *ratio* of two numbers. In this case, it is the ratio of the mental age to the geological age. Now God is almost infinitely wise, but he is also almost infinitely old: and the *ratio* of these two infinities may be a small finite number!"

It was so transparent that we all fell to laughing and burst out together, "—You mean, about the same as the I.Q. of a smart Hungarian!"

The thermodynamics of the solar system, and our prediction of what may happen in it, is incomplete if it does not provide for the evolution of intelligent men, including Hungarians.

CAN INTELLIGENCE SURVIVE?

Looking at this nonclassical evolution of intelligence, one even begins to wonder whether it is such a small Law after all, even from the sun's point of view. Men create lakes and can level mountains; their atomic explosions have already shaken the whole earth's magnetic field; and they send out visible satellites and sensors that now range the solar system. Will the evolution of these powers of intelligence go on increasing? Or must it finally run down, as the sun does, by the great Second Law?

If we think about this problem in the light of the physical and biological regularities of behavior that we now know, it seems to me that we are led to a further rather surprising conclusion: There is no thermodynamic reason why evolution should ever stop. What evolution leads to is the larger and larger control of environment by the organisms, first by genetic natural selection; then, with the growth of societies and language, by cultural natural selection; and finally by brains. And once we pass a certain threshold of brains and intelligence we begin to know how to insulate ourselves against all sorts of environmental changes.

Will the sun slowly decay? As Thornton Wilder suggested in his play *The Skin of Our Teeth,* the coming of the cold may simply provide the stress of necessity for us to learn to use our heat sources more efficiently. Barring catastrophes, such as the possibility that we may kill ourselves by our lack of control over our own collective behavior before we pass *that* threshold, it does not seem impossible that we might get smarter faster than the world runs down, and keep ourselves going and manipulating and developing indefinitely.

It is a little bit like the engineering students' humorous logical proof that hell has a constant temperature. For, they say, it is certain that there is at least one engineer in hell. And if hell did not have a constant temperature, this engineer would be able to use the temperature differences to drive a heat engine, which could run a refrigerator that would keep him cool. But this would thwart the whole purpose of hell—which is absurd! Therefore the assumption must be wrong, and hell must have a constant temperature.

I would simply turn this logic around and say that the solar system does not have a constant temperature everywhere, and never will have: therefore it is not hell. There will always be room for energetic intelligence to continue to make a niche for itself. If we do not blow ourselves up, we can begin to see a new vista of a long cosmic future that might be stretching ahead. Intelligence and its manipulations may be one of the permanent and major cosmic phenomena. The classical thermodynamicists, reasoning from isolated systems, might not have admitted these nonclassical possibilities. But there is a hole here big enough to pass through a cartload of theologians.

The scientific approximations useful in one era are often enlarged into the dominant philosophy of the next. Arguing from isolated systems, Clausius proclaimed the steady increase of disorder in the universe, and Helmholtz took it as a text. Kelvin argued with the geologists that the ages they deduced for the rocks were a physical impossibility, that the sun had only lasted a few million years and only had a little longer to go. The Victorian universe ran down and Victorian biology was hostile, red in tooth and claw.

The consequence was that, a generation later, Henley's cry,

> *"Out of the night that covers me,*
> *Black as the pit from pole to pole,"*

expressed the world view of all brave and unsentimental minds. For the young Russell, in "A Free Man's Worship," there could be nothing but the proud defiance of the irresistible forces:

Brief and powerless is Man's life; on him and all his race the slow, sure doom falls pitiless and dark. Blind to good and evil, reckless of destruction, omnipotent matter rolls on its relentless way; for Man, condemned to-day to lose his dearest, tomorrow himself to pass through the gate of darkness, it remains only to cherish, ere yet the blow falls, the lofty thoughts that ennoble his little day.

The literary formulation of Victorian thermodynamics.

Again and again isolated-system thinking has presented us with mistaken extrapolations about the world and man. Common sense is outraged, but the logic is unanswerable. No wonder that these "objective" conclusions are first taken up, and then often turned against both science and man. But it is time for some of the more ancient errors to be corrected so that we can get a truer view of our place in the world and our uniqueness and powers. Yes, we die; but mankind lives, and may go on living and growing if we can use our intelligence to save ourselves rather than to kill ourselves. Omnipotent matter is plastic to the thinking mind. Our own complexity and importance stand apart from the equations of science but will not be left out. We live in a universe that has created this complexity and somehow cherishes it.

Many of our most sensitive spirits today still see man as the anti-hero, the helpless victim of weapons and wars, of governments and mechanisms and soul-destroying organizations and computers. As indeed he is. But in the midst of this man-made and inhuman entropy, like a Fourth Law of Man, there grows up even in the laboratories the realization that man is also mysterious and elusive, hedged about with indeterminacies, self-determining and perpetual, a lighthouse of complexity and the organizing child of the universe, one equipped and provided for, to stand and choose and act and control and be.

Man is still evolving as explosively as ever; and we are acquiring a new view of his place in the universe, his nature, and his destiny.

Changing Human Nature

The comedians Mike Nichols and Elaine May have a funny dialogue which is supposed to be a long-distance telephone conversation between a New York mother and her son who is a space scientist at Cape Kennedy. The mother calls up her scientist-son; she begins to accuse him of neglecting her, and tells him all her neurotic troubles; finally, she gets so sorry for herself that she cries and will not hang up until he talks baby talk to her just like he used to do when he was a little boy.

Our view of human nature today is in many ways very much like this mother's view of her little boy. The boy has grown up into a spaceman, but we keep thinking of him as though he were still a baby. We are used to the idea that communications are changing, that the international political scene is changing, that science and technology are developing as never before, but for some reason we tend to go on believing that human nature remains the same and always will. Any debate over the cold war, or over social inequality, or over terrorism somewhere, is all too likely to be terminated by someone remarking rather smugly, "Well, after all, human nature never changes."

On sober reflection, probably none of us really believes this. Many of us spend time and money for political persuasion or social reform, hoping to convert other people to different ways of thinking and acting. And we all spend money to educate our children to new goals and abilities that will make them less like little savages. We are never quite sure it will work, but we have hope. This activity would be absurd if we actually thought there was no possibility of changing human nature. The time when we quote these false folk proverbs to ourselves is at that awful hour of five o'clock when we need to be reassured that there will not be any changes in our own status and attitudes.

Nevertheless, the idea that human nature is constant is expressed so often, by everyone from conservative politicians to drama critics, that it may be good now and then to remind ourselves of the extensive evidence—evidence from history as well as evidence from the laboratories today—that shows how easily human behavior can be formed and modified. I am not talking about changes in human knowledge or in the use of knowledge to control nature, which everyone knows about, but about changes in emotional reactions and social behavior that change the kind of friends we are and the kind of cities we make. I think we must conclude that the variability of human nature is much more remarkable than its constancy. It can be shaped by circumstances and culture into almost any form we wish. And today, like everything else, it is changing more rapidly than ever before.

THE CHANGES

In fact, it seems to me that a significant difference in our character and behavior is easy to see in ten generations, and perhaps even in one. Already most of us are shocked and nauseated if we read about the public bloodthirstiness and the torture of men and animals that was still a daily feature of life in the Middle Ages. Yes, we have stooped to such things, and horribly recently; but the mass of mankind repudiates them today. Here is a description of "trial by combat" as it used to be done:

A piece of ground is . . . set out, sixty feet square, and on one side a court is erected for the judges. . . . The champions (for the parties) . . . are dressed in a coat of armour, with red sandals, barelegged from the knee down, bareheaded, with bare arms to the elbow. . . . The battle is thus begun and the combatants are bound to fight until the stars appear in the evening.

Today, the absurdity of this as a method of deciding the rights and wrongs of a civil dispute strikes all of us immediately, but it was still on the books in this form, in Blackstone's *Commentaries on the Laws of England,* as lately as 200 years ago.

Dueling is another bloody custom we have given up surprisingly recently. In France in the 1790's, the number of young men killed in duels is supposed to have been in the tens of thousands per year, so that until it was abolished the custom was much more lethal in that small population than automobile accidents are today. Is human nature still the same? Or are we not appreciably less bloodthirsty now? Less aggressive, even at basketball games? Less touchy about real or fancied insults? In our more advanced cultures almost certainly so. A mutually dependent society cannot afford that kind of behavior any more. The approval of it, the forms, the laws, have changed. And therefore, adaptably, the behavior has changed.

The changes just in the last century in England and America have modified, I believe, all our daily motivations and attitudes. As Robert Maynard Hutchins has said:

Of the two pillars of our society, property and work, the first has now been transformed; it has changed from visible goods into a series of claims; and the second is certain to disappear. We are going to have to live in a world without work, a world without want, a world without disease, and, if we are to live at all, in a world without war.

I think these transformations are one reason why it seems increasingly hard to enjoy nineteenth-century novels any more. All the great classic motives of literature—personal conflict, love and death, ambition and property, mistreatment and revenge, mistaken identities and mislaid messages—have been changed out of recognition just since the beginning of this century. Do we still scheme to outdo the brother in the old man's will? Sometimes, perhaps; but in general, the inflation of status and the hope of inheritance—the themes of Dickens and Jane Austen and the Brontës—have come to seem not merely idle but preposterous as incentives for healthy human beings. The total identification is lost that once made us cry and read on until dawn.

We suddenly realize that what themes are great, or even understandable to us, depends on the inheritance laws and the death rate. When boys and girls die young, with time for one short marriage or none, love and death are linked themes. The ten-child family with the eight-child death rate necessarily produces elegiac stanzas and a market for mournfulness. But now the epic and the ode are gone with the royal patron. And gone with the unchecked sperm and spirochete is the guilt of love and the certain punishment of hearts too warm, by pregnancy and death. How can we understand the old refrains?

Even today, much of our fiction is out-of-date, I think. It is hopeless fiction, to prove we are trapped; or lifeboat fiction, to prove the world is small and ironical; or Greek fiction, to prove our subconscious violence. It is all contrived so obviously to prove a point or to keep us breathless—and it is so false to the subtle causes and continuities of human interrelations and cooperative behavior that we now see daily in the intelligent living people around us.

The same is true, I often feel, with history. It is real, but it is not real for us. Once the U.S. Constitution had been set up specifically to avoid the fatal mistakes of the Athenian and Roman democracies, to create a differently motivated political man, should we not expect our political experience to have major differences from theirs, which the study of their history will hardly teach us?

Any observation of contrasting human groups shows that the child in one culture becomes one sort of man and the child in another culture, another. Change the culture and you change the man. After reading Ruth Benedict and Margaret Mead, does anyone doubt that the child brought up in the easygoing Hawaiian culture would become an easygoing adult? Or that a child brought up in Sparta would become a Spartan adult? What we call national character is nothing more than the perpetuation of certain attitudes as the result of imitation or of the continuity of circumstances. In any country, if you give a group of young men guns, and put them among a helpless population they have been taught to call inferior, and promise immunity for whatever acts they commit, you will create murderers and sadists, whether the men are Americans or Japanese running prison camps in the

Pacific, or young Nazis, or the French Foreign Legion, or political or racial terrorists of any other nationality. And it will take a generation to get over it. In this sense, human nature is indeed constant. Its constancy lies in its adaptability to the environments we set up.

Even in the same community, we see different types of character produced by different homes and schools. A superstitious household, full of medieval devil stories and tales of the ghost Aunt Martha saw, produces a superstitious child. An old-fashioned orphan asylum makes a dull child. A Montessori school makes an alert, manipulative child. A kibbutz school makes a special kind of matter-of-fact, group-oriented child.

It is perhaps only in the last century or two, since Rousseau and Pestalozzi and Montessori, that leaders have begun to think seriously about how they could change society systematically by changing the education of the children. In America, this notion was central in the minds of many early reformers. For example, George Ripley, who was the leader of the famous Brook Farm experiment in Masssachusetts in the 1840's, was such an optimist that he thought he knew how to reform the worst savages. He said:

> Place the savage in a different situation; let the first words that fall upon his ear be those of Christian gentleness and peace; let him be surrounded by loving and generous hearts; another spirit will be manifested; and you would almost say that he had been endowed with another nature.

Somewhat romantic, of course. The colony foundered from an excess of romanticism in all directions. But the fundamental idea is certainly correct.

IN THE LABORATORY

But what is more important, these historical and philosophical conclusions are beginning to be supported now by laboratory experiments. The ease with which all our mammalian behavior can be shaped or damaged is one of the central features of the experimental psychology of the mid-Twentieth century. The psychologist Hebb and his followers have shown that the sensory deprivation of young animals leads to disorganized perceptions and reactions for the rest of their lives. Harlow at Wisconsin has shown that monkeys who have been reared with artificial "mothers," made of cloth and wire and a baby bottle, become permanently psychotic and cannot even mate when they grow up; or if they are then impregnated artificially, they make no attempt to mother the babies they give birth to. Lorenz in Germany has shown that a duckling follows its mother because it has been "imprinted" to her shortly after hatching, but that it can be imprinted equally well to a mechanical toy or a graduate student. In another direction, Held, formerly at Brandeis and now at M.I.T., has shown how rapidly we human beings can adapt our behavior to compensate for systematic distortions of the external world. And Skinner at Harvard has shown that dogs and pigeons can be trained in a few minutes, by his "rapid-reinforcement" methods, without any punishment, to do tricks that dogs and pigeons never did in the history of the world before. And that human beings, with these rapid teaching methods and with the "programmed teaching" based on them, can likewise learn many things much faster and easier than was ever possible with older methods. Moore, now at Rutgers, has recently shown that with such methods children at ages two to four can learn to read and write on electric typewriters, and are soon typing out their own poems and stories.

There have been many revolutions in our time, but I think that in the long run this psychological revolution that we see beginning here in the theory and practice of shaping behavior of the young will be the most important revolution of all for the success and happiness of man on this planet.

Real teaching is *so* easy. The old ideas of severity and punishment are *so* irrelevant. "Efficient learning is never hard," says the psychologist, Kubie. The child is as eager to imitate us as the duckling is to follow the duck. He is instantly interested in what we are interested in. The girl learns the enjoyment of cooking —or the lack of enjoyment—from her mother as easily as the boy learns baseball and automobiles and war from his father. It is in the air they breathe. In fact, the reason our various theories of education have neither helped us nor hurt us very much is that each generation has succeeded so spontaneously and so closely in imitating the one before—all the way down to its theories of education. Our harassed schoolteachers and droning lecturers have simply created over and over again a new generation of bored students and harassed schoolteachers and droning lecturers. Nothing we do can make one generation very much better—or very much worse—than the one before, except, for the first time, an operationally effective theory of education.

I know that many thoughtful people are opposed to the use of these new methods. Brainwashing, they say; treating children as if they were pigeons. Deterministic and dangerous, they say; destroying the children's free will. (I once knew of a farm family that refused to have any books in the house, except the Bible, for very similar reasons. Powerful new reading and teaching devices have always been feared.)

But I think the issue in this case is not really one of the morality or determinism of more effective methods. Good teaching—and better teaching—has always been a most moral obligation, approved and commanded by the churches and the laws. And teaching has always been deterministic and dangerous. Harsh and stupid parents and schoolmasters have wrecked many a child's life—while society kept its hands off. Do we need to say what everyone knows—that this determinism of consequences is implicit in the nature of free will? The freedom of one moment, the choice and control of circumstances, is always used to determine the next. And the freedom of one generation, its choice and control of education, is always used to determine the next.

No; the issue here, I think, is that many of us do not trust our school boards and our teachers to use the new methods wisely. We fear that these easy and almost automatic techniques will be allowed to drive out human warmth and variety from the classroom; or will shape our children's learning into a frozen pattern, past some point of no return, where their behavior and their own eventual teaching will no longer be flexible or intelligent enough to meet new crises or to evolve further.

This would be fatal, of course. But a good automobile driver is helped, not harmed, by better technical devices, and a good driver will use all his intelligence not to destroy his later freedom or his children's freedom by driving into a ditch. Is not an intelligent society then helped by better technical devices, as well?

The cure for our fears is not resistance to the new teaching techniques, but insistence on trying them carefully, observing

them, and then discussing and deciding how they can be fitted
in to give children a faster and easier education in things that are
best taught this way, while allowing teachers and parents not
less but more time for the other education that we call variety
and humanity and warmth and love.

TEACHING AS THE CHOICE OF CHANGE

Since caveman times, we must have known that human behavior is adaptable. We have always tried to teach our children
what we wanted them to learn and what we wanted them to be.
The only difference today is that it looks as though we may soon
find out how to be successful at it. It seems to me that these
changes in human nature and the possibilities and choices ahead
form one of the most interesting subjects in the world for
contemplative men. "We know what we are, we know not what
we may become," said the Christian philosopher, thinking of
heaven. But I would say, if we do not know what we may
become, we cannot know what we are. The maturing child only
begins to realize who he is when his imagination and his planning begin to turn toward the man he will become. It is the
same with a maturing society.

Evidently the time is approaching when our whole society will
begin to be self-conscious about what it may become, when we
will begin to choose it deliberately instead of accidentally. We
now realize that the society we can and will become is shaped
by what we teach, by the kind of human nature we are producing
day by day in our children. This means that there is a problem
of choice in our teaching, a collective problem far larger than
any single wise educator can solve for us. This old and yet
remarkably new discovery of the plasticity of human nature
means that all of us—natural and social scientists, psychologists
and teachers, historians and writers, students of economics and
politics, government and university leaders, philosophers and
citizens—all of us will be deciding and need to be deciding what
kind of human nature and what kind of personal and social
relationships we want to teach our children to have, so that
they will be able to make a better society in turn for themselves.

We realize that we have to reexamine our attitudes—attitudes which are a primary part of what is taught—all the way down to the cradle. How do we want our children to learn to behave whenever they are frustrated by a mechanical toy or by a playmate? Do we want them to have perfect patience? Or to have patience for a little while? Or to stamp on the floor and strike out for their needs? Should we teach a child to say, "Mine!" at a certain age; or at another age to say, "You can have it"? Should we teach him to strive for leadership; or for group cooperation?

Different answers to these questions have been preferred over the course of history, and are preferred today in different families. One set of answers may produce conformists, while another set may produce maverick children who do not get along on teams and committees and who may be branded juvenile delinquents by the standards of their times. A dynamic society obviously needs a lot of this kind of independence—but not too much! What is the best mixture—and how do we train children both to fulfill their individual potentialities and yet to cooperate enough to keep their society functioning effectively?

Americans have one answer for such questions, Russians another, and Chinese another. No wonder we have different social structures. No wonder we are mystified and dismayed by each others' reactions! Will we have to reduce some of this variation in childhood training between nations, so that it will be easier to trust each other and easier not to get frightened into blowing each other up? Or will it be possible to keep some of the differences, so that the world will not be too dull?

In shaping our cultural inheritance, we have always made our children in almost our own cultural image. Their imitation is so spontaneous that we do it in spite of ourselves. There are variations and improvements in successive generations, but the parents' basic cultural image has been the only image, at a given moment in social time and space, that we knew would work together in all its parts.

But in a time like the present, of rapid changes and new demands, an intelligent conservatism that really *conserves* our society may come to demand rapid and intelligent change. When a man is about to be run over by an automobile, or when a world is about to be blown up, real conservatism may demand that he jump out of the way quickly. And collectively today, we may reach a point of no return by not changing fast enough, just as we may reach one by changing too fast. A radical and ill-considered plunge into Utopianism might destroy our culture, but it is also certain to be destroyed if we go on sticking to our old military belligerence or our old uncontrolled human fertility. Our only safety therefore lies in thinking about what is best to do, in which directions we should change and adapt rapidly and in which directions we should emphasize stability.

Our situation in this problem of social design is somewhat like that of those men who took such a bold step in designing a novel kind of government for the United States. In fact, we might paraphrase *The Federalist* papers by saying, "It seems to have been reserved to the people of this generation to decide the important question, whether societies of men are really capable or not, of establishing good *teaching* to shape a better society from reflection and choice, or whether they are forever destined to depend, for their social training and social structure, on imitation and accident." It is time to set up the best new design we can, with care but with confidence in what we are trying to do. As Washington said, "Let us raise a standard to which the wise and honest can repair. The event is in the hands of God."

It is not really going to be so hard to decide what we want to do in our teaching. Our problem, as we begin to come to the end of national wars and to move out into a still uneasy truce for the world, will resemble that of an ex-soldier who has finally got his discharge papers and has to decide what kind of life he wants next. Like him, we may be uncertain whether to take it easy for awhile, or to go on for more education, or to start a new job, or to do several of these at once. And we may try many new things, whether we are sure we want to go on with all of them or not. We may try to train the children for new artistic or scientific adventures, for space exploration or ocean exploration or experimental colonies. We will certainly try to use education to change some of the things we do not like about our present life, such as juvenile delinquency and unemployment. And we will be bored and restless unless we make some fairly magnificent plans for guiding our almost boundless energies in developing and unifying the world. But I think we cannot look too far into the future, but will simply have to trust our own developing culture—as an individual trusts his own developing body—to go on, with the useful and intelligent responses we have already developed, to deal with future problems as they come up.

NEW VIEWS OF THE NATURE OF MAN

These thoughts about the recent changes and the possible future changes in human nature take on additional significance if they are seen as part of our new picture of who and what man is, in the larger cosmic and evolutionary sense. Gauguin asked, in the title of one of his paintings, "Where do we come from? Who are we? Where are we going?" These are the central questions for the real understanding of human nature.

Inspiration and desperation, religion, myth, and poetry used to be the only source of answers to these questions. Today the answers can be based on more factual evidence, from a wide variety of different disciplines, and we find the story is quite different. The discovery of nuclear energy alone has changed our whole view of our past, our powers, and our prospects.

Astronomy, chemistry, and evolution now tell us that life is not a unique event dating from 4004 b.c., but something old and almost inevitable, with billions of years behind it and billions of years ahead, something perhaps repeated many times elsewhere in the universe. Biology tells us that, in this pattern, our complex brains with their manipulative and verbal intelligence have evolved rather suddenly and recently, and are evolving still.

In technology, we now realize we are not running out of energy as we had thought, but have fission and fusion power enough for millions of years. The earth is ours, we have reached its ends; and our satellites have begun to range the solar system and will take men to the moon. We have begun to acquire the biological keys of life and death, with the increasing elimination of disease and the potential control of our own population, and with the beginnings of the chemical manipulation of heredity.

And all over the globe, we have suddenly discovered we are one society, indivisible, for life or death. The nations all have a new intensity of interaction, with new levels of communication and involvement, new cooperation, new dangers, and new co-operative efforts at control.

Are not these all aspects of what man is? What may he become?

In many fields we can discern a new potentiality for shaping the future. This includes our new powers of genetic and biological manipulation, the new psychological shaping of behavior in the ways we have been discussing, powerful new systematic methods of problem solving in mathematics and the sciences, and new computer calculations and guidance for science, automation, communications, and management.

And I think mankind is showing a new level of will and purpose and design, a new feeling that he is the one responsible for himself. Around the world we are finally beginning to make thorough inventories and longer-range and more confident planning and endeavor, in industrial development and national and economic development and food supply and population control. Even at the very heart of the intellectual enterprise, there is a new self-reliance and personalism in philosophy and mathematics and the sciences. We now realize that in perception, it is we who map the world within ourselves. In discovering the nature of things, it is we who choose the problems and who must be convinced by the proofs. In decision, it is we who face the existential imperative to choose and act.

I believe this grand restructuring of our situation quite reverses the older philosophical views of man in several ways.

We used to think of ourselves as orphans in the world. Now we discover that we are children of the universe, that it has been creating and supporting us for a long time and can go on doing so. We were meant to be here, so to speak.

We thought we were insignificant. Now we discover that we are the most complicated thing in creation, as far as we know.

We thought we were disinherited. Now we discover that we have been given power and resources beyond imagining—the power of the sun itself—to do what we want with.

We thought we were helpless, bound by our animal inheritance, or by the darkness of our twisted subconscious, to irredeemable social organizations or to irrational follies and wars. Now we discover that it is culture that shapes our minds and actions, and that better education can lead to better actions, and that consequently we are free to make of ourselves and our children what we choose. There is an incredible amount of social engineering to be done, to make social structures that will give us freedom and yet keep us from killing each other; but it is now clear, on these and other grounds, that it can be done.

I think this revolution in philosophical attitudes that is coming out of the laboratories has not been widely appreciated but is even more important than the great technological revolutions of this century. This new position of intellectual man, in astronomy, in biology, and in psychology and the other sciences, opens the door to a new sense of human freedom. We have a new picture of man's place, his powers, his destiny, and his responsibility. Just as our perception of the external world transcends our internal accidents of construction, so our powers now begin to transcend our biological accidents of origin. It is time to stand up free, with awareness and confidence and choice, to shape, from now on, the further development of what we will become.

There are many ways to make an unstable society and to kill ourselves, but I think that there are also many different kinds of future that are possible and nonlethal and delightful. In fact, I believe it quite likely that we may evolve from one kind of future to another over the centuries, once we learn the basic social rules that will keep us from collective self-destruction. We will be able to try out several of the infinite number of possible social forms, as we go through our long life's day that extends ahead of us for millions or billions of years. Planning a good society as far ahead as we can see, does not mean that our adventures have ended; they have just begun. Human nature is growing up. As we put behind us the accidents and tears of childhood squabbles and the wooden swords and shields, and begin to try on our new space-pilot's uniform, so to speak, we begin to see what we can teach ourselves and what we can really become with new self-control over our new and adult powers.

The time is now; the future branches out indefinitely from this interaction and this moment.

Start Here

We used to say that the trouble with teen-agers was that they were living too much in the present. Grow up!, we said. Widen your horizons, begin to see and plan where you are going, if you want to become adults.

But today it is perfectly clear that millions of people have fallen into just the opposite error. Many of us have forgotten how to live in the present at all. We are racing like mad to get somewhere else. Or we read, read, read. This morning I looked in the mirror at a man who had run through two pounds of newsprint for breakfast. I was suddenly startled to see that his face was not set in type.

Today our horizons have widened marvelously, and it is good. We see and plan as never before. But we often forget to savor and appreciate. Some of us go day after day without really looking at our families. We fail to taste the immediacy, the intensity, of rock, bark, plaster, tablecloths, an eye, the smell of onions. The Zen Buddhist is right. Perhaps we need a punch in the nose to remind us that the universe around us all the time is saying, Look! See!

I know there are many who believe that we cannot help it, that a loss of awareness is inevitable under the conditions of modern life. Some say it is the natural result of being surrounded by cheap and tasteless products. Others blame it on our mobility and multiplied communications. Others say it is due to our unreal abstractions, our neurotic explanations and political catchphrases. And who can doubt but that the hard objective philosophy of our age has exerted a constant pressure to make us belittle the immediate and the personal?

All these factors add up. Nevertheless, it seems to me that the crux of the problem for any individual, for you and me, is not a question of vast forces but of our personal practice and habit. All anyone needs to do to reacquire awareness is simply to start practicing it, to open his eyes again and see. Pause. Breathe. Look. Marvel. To live in the present, all you need to do is to say to yourself something like, "Start here!"

Is not this the real principle?—to start here and now with yourself, here and now in the living breathing relations about you? It sounds trivial, of course. Where else can we start? But this kind of nondirective prod to our attention can sometimes work wonders. The longer I have thought about it, the more I have become convinced that this is a profound idea. It reminds us to stop grasping at shadows, to put the subjective and human back in the center where they belong. When that is done, the complex and distant can extend the immediate, the symbolic can enrich the tangible, the abstract can add to the concrete rather than driving it out.

Today science, from mathematics and physics on, is acquiring a more subjective cast. Biology celebrates the individual; anthropology emphasizes his creative role in ongoing cultural evolution. Perception theory is showing that perception is mixed with action, linking environment with self and self with environment inseparably. Psychology is seeing the brain not as the slave but as the director of its parts. And philosophy is teaching us that it is the *here* of being and action that underlies anything further that can be said about the world. We all recognize that it is our objective understanding of the world that has given us our power and achievements and freedom from superstition and fear; but it is the subjective that senses and verifies the objective, that touches and loves, that creates and pleases, and that we ignore at the peril of our immortal happiness.

We have not always taught this, or believed it. Perhaps that is the reason for some of the great psychological strains in our society today. I think what we need to do to correct them is to cry out over and over again to ourselves and our children, "Start here! Start here!," until we learn to do it habitually, until by practice we realize again that it is immediate here-and-now perception and interaction and creation that is at the living center of things and that alone can give validation and meaning to the whirling problems and achievements of our times. Personal reality is the bedrock from which confident action arises. The adoption of an attitude of subjective immediacy, a Start Here attitude, no longer needs to be regarded as an escape from the world or as something bordering on self-delusion, but rather as a way of restoring psychological wholeness, acquiring a new single-mindedness and intensity, and appreciating and acting in the world more effectively.

I am not trying to claim any unique merit for the Start Here form of words, of course. The change from the objective to the subjective point of view is like the change from inattention to listening, or from distraction to concentration, and we can all make such changes without any motto or formula, if we have had sufficient practice and incentive. But still it helps when we say to the children: Pay attention! Sometimes they do. Start Here is the same kind of alert-signal to ourselves, to pay attention to what *is*.

I think it is extremely interesting to look in more detail at what might happen to our image of ourselves, and to our relation to the world and the people around us, if we began to take the Start Here change of attitude seriously. The subject obviously has not only scientific but religious overtones, with a relation particularly to some of the Christian teachings with their strong emphasis on personal immediacy and action. I think we will see that the adoption of this attitude can lead to a startling and delightful shift in self-perspective because of its emphasis on living in the present with enjoyment and spontaneity and choice. It can reemphasize for us the dynamic and "becoming" character of the world and the spreading circles of relationship and change by which our personal force in every desire and gesture reshapes the future afresh at every instant.

THE SENSE OF PERSONAL UNIQUENESS

For example, if one says to himself, "Start here!," surely it can only reinforce his sense of personal uniqueness, of individuality and decision. To Start Here, anyone can start only as himself, as he is now. We are not merely interchangeable role players. Is there anyone who is not, by his own special inheritance and history, a very special person with a very special preparation? If you are the one with the Polish grandmother, if you are the one who had to transfer to Belmont High School for your senior year, that alone should give you some unusual insights, sociological and educational and humorous. I celebrate the varieties among men. Vive les différences! Everyone sees, and tells, how poor his own preparation was in one way or another. Nevertheless, by it have you not acquired strange talents, friend?—strange, but curiously useful? For you are unique; yourself; and after you have cast a little sigh for the roads not taken, think instead of the remarkable road you took.

For this unique past, yours or mine, surely makes possible some unique things we can do in the present, starting here. Life flings us out randomly like seeds into all sorts of crevices, high and low. Some fall on rocks and some among thorns, while others have the still worse fate of being overnourished and over-protected. But the evolutionary hope is that every seed, by its very combination of accidents, will find in itself some new potentiality for development that will enlarge the experience of the whole race. We have regarded the survival of the fittest as a cruel doctrine; but it is a doctrine of life as much as a doctrine of death. It means the survival of wing and brain, of the most adaptable, the most enduring, the most anticipatory, the most enjoying, the most diversely communicating with the universe. The picture of man's evolution is not that of a huddled community waiting to be eaten, but that of explorers always learning how to live beyond the fringes. In the rock itself, one tough flower may find a hard niche that in a time of storms preserves the species. What seemed catastrophe becomes the single hope of salvation.

Many of us have trouble believing in our own special potentialities for handling our special circumstances. We are reluctant to insist that we have a different vision. Our novelists, ignorant of the work of the world, have preached violence, futility, and mechanism, until we have almost forgotten our individual creative worth. We forget that even where opportunities are few, love can make a Nancy Hanks, and perseverance a Nathaniel Bowditch. Even in a kitchen, one can share the excitement of a great pie. Even enmeshed in government, one can find time to meditate and be aware. Start Here is a unique present from the universe to each of us, and all it asks in return is our unique response. There are many ways of life that you can never be; but there is one that you can be; and are, beginning now.

Almost everyone has met a few men or women who seem to be shaping their lives in this way around some kind of Start Here rule for themselves. You know them by their behavior; resourceful, direct, productive, easy. The neuroses drop away, the atmosphere changes. They speak with confidence, not as quoters and apologizers. You feel the force when you are in their presence. One might say they have the straightforwardness of animals—or angels.

This simplicity and power is characteristic of the well-established forms of organic life. The organic world has learned to act with decision, to say its Yea or Nay clearly and completely, to go forward with all it knows from where it is. "Start here!" is essentially the only command in evolution. What life says to the chromosomes in every cell is, Start Here. Even before there was life, what life said to the pre-organic molecules was, Start Here. And today when our evolutionary development is not through the body and the chromosomes so much as through the intellect and the brain, what life says to every mind is still, Start Here.

From this point of view, Start Here is not an inspirational phrase but simply a factual description of how the world successfully works and of how you work, whether you are conscious of it or not. But is not this in itself a source of reassurance? It makes a man feel that his own forces can play a role with the other evolutionary forces in life and society instead of being wasted in wishing against them.

THE END OF THE PAST

Start Here can also give us a sense of relief at realizing truly that the past is past. The past should illuminate our actions, but often we let it clog them. Many a person is still busy reliving the old fight with father or sister or brother, still replaying the missed love or the angry bargaining or the sad mistake over and over again with curses and justifications. Which of your muscles is drawn up now?—your eyelids?—your shoulders? Realize and relax. Most of us crouch or squint a little all day long, keeping half-tensed for tomorrow's blow or for the blow of fifteen years ago. No wonder we are worn out when night comes. No wonder we cannot sleep. The old fears and excuses, conscious or, worse, half-conscious, gnaw at the edges of every active thought.

I do not blame you. I do not blame anyone. What is blame but a reopening of wounds? And I have no certain cure. Once we are caught in these old circles with ourselves, it is hard to get out by any method or any medicine. And no formula can remove real grief or real pain.

Yet with the past on your back, is there anything else that is any more effective, really, than to say, Start Here? The old debts are wiped out, forgiven; we start with the cash on hand. It is a shift of perspective, a change of situation that does not have to be waited for year after year: a fresh beginning that you have only to reach out and grasp, now. It can help get rid of the vampire worries by exposing them for the ghosts they are. It puts the attention back on the present awareness and the present straightening out and the present action, which is the only action you, or anyone, can ever take. You "wash your face, and you brush your hair, and start all over again." Sometimes this can get the mechanism off dead center at last; and the sense of relief can be enormous. When it comes, it is not merely relief; it is re-life.

THE CONTINUAL CREATION OF CHANGE

But Start Here not only says to put yourself here, but to start. It is a dynamic and operational attitude, not a static one. We tend to forget that our slightest actions send reverberations across the world. A human being is, so to speak, a continuously operating push button of change. All the amplifications and effects that can be produced by human interaction are to some degree at the command of each of us.

It is easy to see, for example, that if you delay even a fraction of a second at a stoplight, perhaps to admire a red dress, it can change the sequence of cars at that stoplight and the next ones and the next, across the country to every airport, and across the world! Within a week, there are different deaths and different planes missed everywhere; different boys meet girls in elevators and have different love affairs and different children. Will one of them be born a Hitler? A Gandhi? Different ideas are hastened or delayed.

Sterne and Tolstoy were fascinated by these vast mechanical consequences of small random causes, and many modern writers have used them to show the pointlessness of human effort. Absurd, frightening, that for want of a nail, the horse is lost, the general is lost, the war is lost! And yet this simple tracing of events from a single cause does not even begin to suggest how complex the interconnections really are. Every physiological and psychological event in your household from the instant of your waking contributes to that pause at the stoplight. From your waking?—from your birth. Every event in the history of man. We live in a billionfold kaleidoscope of infinite potentialities, changing at every moment in its causal details, with many of the changes hidden in these billionfolded selecting and amplifying heads of ours. The very idea of a detailed determinist prediction of all this private amplification becomes absurd. Just the private events in all our human brains are too complex for all our brains to know. This is where our freewill lies, not in any indeterminacy of physical and chemical cause and effect. Every moment branches out into a vast and unpredictable future that you are changing just by reading this, or daydreaming, or blinking your eyes.

With all this flux, it is surprising that the world is as steady as it is. It is fortunate for us that there are smoothing and stabilizing effects; and laws and schedules that permit us to predict and plan; and some constancy in our attachments. It is fortunate that we can sleep and wake to fresh mornings and fresh beginnings, or we should go mad.

Nevertheless, this ever-developing flux is all produced by the amplification of small causes, and this is an essential realization for those who have the Start Here attitude. Start Here is the trigger of causality. What those pointless mechanical consequences really demonstrate is that the causal chains are working. And therein lies the hope of action to contradict the pointlessness. The world is a biological amplifying system, just as the brain and the muscles are in their own responsive way. We are able to move our muscles intentionally and fairly accurately in spite of their unpredictable little variations and tremors. We can move the world as well, in the direction of our real desires.

This may seem dubious, in view of the terrifying quiverings and spasms of our society today, but nevertheless the world is undeniably becoming more and more responsive to commitment and intelligence. Men are not horseshoe crabs, to remain unchanged for a hundred million years. A touch, a germ, an idea catches fire, and the old systems are swept away and new systems sweep into being. It is evolution in action. This shows in great things, in the development of new nations and perhaps even in the stalemated dangers of the old; but it also shows in small things, in the amplified influence of any dedicated person. The cooperative movement grows out of the self-help efforts of a few Rochdale weavers. A Budapest kindergarten teacher shows five-year-olds how to examine and ask questions, and they become some of the greatest scientists we have.

Trust the network. Start Here, with confidence. What is your personal force for? You are a part of living matter, part of the biosphere, and we are all members one of another, imitating and responding. It is a tremendous realization. You live in the eternal now, a choosing one, triggering all about you into continually new patterns in this flux of choice and change. By tomorrow morning it will have begun to take effect, as quietly and surely as the unfolding of a chromosome.

It is all a vast operational train of proof that we exist. As the philosophy of existentialism might say, I act, therefore I am. It is true that some men need to exaggerate in order to prove visibly that they can act, and do exist. The three-year-old must say No, No, No, to prove he is an independent person. The new driver needs to gun the engine and then jam on the brakes to prove that he can move with smooth control down the road. But with practice, we find more subtle and effective ways of Starting Here in action. When we realize that every move reverberates around the globe, and when we become conscious of the dynamic changes that we induce in those around us with every gesture of affection or leadership, as well as with every pause at the stoplight, it no longer takes bizarre and dramatic actions to convince us of our powers.

THE CHRISTIAN ASPECT

We have hinted at some of the religious parallels earlier, but it is interesting to go on to see more explicitly how similar this approach is to the religious and, specifically, the Christian statement of the relation of man to the world. The spreading circle of social consequences from every act is one of the things that Christianity especially emphasized. Thought of as a social theory, Christianity could be said to be concerned with the molecular elements in social change, with the relation between individual action and social reaction and with how a restructuring of the individual acts could result in restructuring the society. From a secular and psychological point of view, the Gospels might be regarded as primary texts on the principles of social dynamics and social engineering. In these terms, the first part of the discovery of Jesus is "Start here!"; and the second part is "Give now!"

All one discovery, really: Start Here, now, with yourself; and Start Here, at this place in the human network. They are the personal and the social sides of the same coin—the self-propagating coin which is both the elementary act and the medium of exchange of that vast commerce which is social creation. To build a new life or a new community or a new world, Start Here and Give Instantly.

Surely no other teacher has had so intensely this dynamic and operational attitude. The Confucian says, Behave thyself. The Zen Buddhist says, Awaken thyself. The Greek says, Know thyself. Jesus says, Change thyself.

Today the revivalists still preach a guilt-ridden and crisis variety of Start Here, but until recently, at least, many other churchmen have seemed to slide away from this dynamic immediacy in the teachings of Jesus. Again and again in many different ways he says: Begin where you are. You don't have to be rich or influential or brilliant; even fishermen can turn the world upside down; if they can, you can. It is a radical idea! You don't even have to have been good; your sins are forgiven, forget the guilt and fear; start here. Let the dead bury their dead, but take up your bed now, and walk. Go, and sin no more.

Jesus does not give us a discourse on the nature of the universe, he gives us a set of active verbs. And yet what better discourse on the real nature of the universe could there be? A more surprising thing is that he does not even seem to be much concerned with ethics and rules of conduct, compared to his concern with operational decision. He says, I do not need to tell you the commandments; the theologians spend all day arguing about those things; but you know already which was neighbor to him that fell among thieves. The problem has never been to know the good, but to do it. The great barrier is psychological, the barrier to action. Is it easier to say: Your old mistakes are over with, or to say: Take up your bed and walk? Jesus says they are identical in operational meaning.

Directness was the essence: Start Here. The test for admitting his disciples, those men who were to change the world, was not an I.Q. test. It was a test of their readiness to act: Follow me. Those who did were in. And when he sent them out to teach others, he did not give them lecture notes or enrichment materials. He said: Speak from the heart. Be direct. Carry no papers. Sincerity and wholeness come across better than fearful precautions and elaborate plans. Concentrate on your immediate audience and on what they want most deeply to hear. Let the focus of your eye be single and your whole body will be full of light.

Could anything be more flattering to the hearer, more intensely interacting with him, more winning, more irresistible? It is a social powerhouse. These were not mumbling philosophers but men who cared. I suspect one of the reasons for the rapid spread of the early Church was the immediacy and power of this Start Here habit of mind, with its sense of release, its directness, and its confidence in final effectiveness.

START HERE AS RESPONSE

What are we to Start Here to do? This was the second part of Jesus' program. His answer is again an operational answer, rather than any discussion of ultimate purposes. It is something like Give Now, or Respond Immediately. That is, essentially, Start Here again, but in terms of interaction with other human beings.

It is interesting to see that, today, psychology is also telling us to respond immediately. The fastest methods of teaching animals or children, for example, are based on giving them a little positive response, a reward signal or "reinforcement," every time they move a little closer to the desired goal. With human beings, an encouraging word suffices, or perhaps a nod or the flattering attention of the eyes. If repeated sufficiently often and with sufficient care to lead always in the desired direction, these signals can "shape the behavior" of the pupil or teach the lesson to him rapidly and without mistakes. It is the principle of social gatherings that we all know, that a man will turn his conversation more and more in your direction if you keep responding to him.

What we respond to is responsive direct attention, and this is the most valuable and the most stimulating reward that one mind can offer to another, whether the motive is education, love, or conversion. Without at least a little of it, animals and human beings can go crazy; but with it, they lean toward you and blossom like the rose. To love your neighbor as yourself is evidently a technical tool of persuasion as well as a moral command.

We all know this, really. Who do you try hardest to listen to, the one who shouts or the one who speaks intimately? Who have you loved most or learned most from? Wasn't it the one who responded most sensitively to your mind and needs? Every lover experiences the persuasiveness of loving "as yourself," not pretending or holding back, but giving your full quickness and honesty and humor and responding in every pore with attentive eyes and hands and heart. It is enough to make a man give you half his income—as every woman knows. The technique of conquering by yielding was learned by women and slaves long ago, which is perhaps why Christianity was their religion first. This is the lesson a child learns earliest, as he wraps his father around his finger. We see it in education all the time, from the other side. Children are easy to teach—as soon as you love them "as yourself!" They pick up instantly our real personal enthusiasms, baseball and cooking and cars, where we enjoy showing off and sharing our creative skills. It is mind-to-mind contagion.

Start Here is a reminder that we could be infecting other people all the time in this engaging way, "as ourselves." But do we do it? Rarely. We go on in our clumsy jungle way, trying to coerce and dominate. Not listening, but shouting. Not perceptive, but prying. We are unwilling to look into each others' eyes; and we hold back communication rather than building it up into an easy laughing channel. Often we fail to respond to our children at all except when they are complaining or quarreling. No wonder they keep doing it for us! And as teachers, we forget how infectious real education is. We are insecure, formal, obsessed with control, not looking directly and speaking personally to them as one candid and uncertain human being to another.

No wonder Jesus was the prophet of children. They were entranced at feeling, perhaps for the first time, a direct and personal response.

We see that the persuasive effects of immediate and sensitive response are not either religious or psychological mysteries. They are familiar laws of human behavior that can be observed by anyone in a single minute of interaction if he will only look.

One can also extend these reflections to larger social situations, for the Start Here response is the kind of "feedback," in modern terminology, that can help to integrate and stabilize whole chains of social interaction. Flavor your sauce to please their palates, and every teen-ager will rush to your hamburger stand and will tell others about it. Today, the redesign or stabilization of our whole society may depend on our cleverness in setting up personal and educational and political feedback-chains of response, so that our spontaneous reactions nurture and reassure each other instead of threatening each other. Threats are not in human nature any more than cooperation; what is in human nature is response. One can see many chains of spontaneous and mutually satisfying responses in a good marriage and in a good community; they could make a good world, as well.

Does not biological organization show us this same lesson, over and over again? If Start Here is a sort of instantaneous principle of evolution, Give Now is the local principle of symbiosis or of any kind of well-knit biological organization. Start with those around you, say the cells. Is it hard to be good to one's neighbor or children? It must have seemed so to the isolated one-celled animals, devouring and being devoured. But when creatures grow up to the multicellular stage, cooperation and communication between the cells cease to be matters of self-sacrifice and crazy piety, so to speak; they become easy and instantly rewarding and fun. It is a little surprising to realize that the smartest brain must be made of ignorant cells. They are better supported, more effective, yet more individualized, than any of them would be alone. How is it done? Simply by instant responses between them.

I take this as the model and exemplar of what an intelligent society could be. Whenever even two people start giving to each other and working for each other, these qualities and rewards immediately appear—greater mutual benefit, greater ease, and greater individual development at the same time. They appear as soon as a couple begins to work together, or a family, or a neighborhood, or a nation. The great creative teams of American scientists exhibit them. The European Common Market exhibits them. By mutual giving with those around us, we begin to make a kind of local Utopia, where the benefits of cooperative action are so obvious that giving and sharing cease to be self-sacrificing or difficult, and suddenly become as marvelously easy as they are between lovers, so that response becomes happiness and happiness becomes response and development.

SENSING

The Start Here point of view finally and most satisfyingly reminds us not only to act but also to appreciate.

Start Here, says awareness, in its quiet way. The only time there is, is now. The only place for you is here. You have an appointment first with the present. Where are you going so very fast? Had you forgotten that you have a rendezvous with life, here, now, now? If you do not know how to enjoy the being and the becoming of the present instant, with all its interrelated details and active potentialities waiting to be awakened, how can you ever get to a being and a becoming that you will know how to enjoy better?

Some of us used to play a game we called "Best Indian." We would listen with the other children to see who could hear the faintest and the most different sounds, the distant planes or the clock in another room or the faint clicking of an insect's walk. How many of us still pause occasionally now to listen to our world with the same intensity? This total receptiveness must be a part of what Ryo-Nen means when she says,

> *Ask me no more,*
> *Only listen to the voice of pines and cedars,*
> *when no wind stirs.*

On whatever pinnacles of release or success you may have hoped for, you will never hear a more subtle range of sounds than you can hear now, if you will only listen. Never smell a more subtle range of smells, if you will only sense them. Never see a wider field of vision or more delicate structures or more subtle colors than you see now, if you will only be still and be aware. Start Here.

And yet the greatest reward comes in being aware not merely of the static moment but of the dynamic moment, the evolving present of choice and change. The role of change, in various philosophies and religions, has undergone many twists in the course of history. Some doctrines have emphasized meaningless flux, some have emphasized meaningless cycles of birth and death, some have emphasized immobile contemplation, some have emphasized sudden conversion and bold action. But it seems to me that the idea of evolution in action, of evolutionary immediacy, gives us something different from all of these, the awareness of a dynamic *now* of change and growth in which all the world's past and future come to a present focus continually developing through decision and action. Mystics and religious contemplatives who have stressed awareness have often omitted this dynamic and acting aspect of the world's reality, but surely such an omission is just as lopsided as any activist's omission of the contemplative aspect.

The idea of evolutionary immediacy might even make the religiously minded see God in a different way. The God of a continuing ever-present evolution is not someone outside the universe or someone to be met only in the future. Thoreau saw this clearly when he said, "God Himself culminates in the present moment, and will never be more divine in the lapse of all the ages." Such a God is not some kind of watchmaker, as the old apologists mechanically wished us to suppose. They were as deceived as all the other mechanists, from not looking closely enough at the flowers of the field. The factory that makes the parts of a flower is inside, and is not a factory but a development. God is more like a chromosome, or a thought, than a watchmaker. The creative principle of the universe and its organization and intelligence is not an external principle but an internal one. All of the past that we can ever know is contained in the world at this instant. All of the evolving potentialities of the future are contained in the world at this instant. And men are the carriers of this active potentiality as much as any. The creative principle is inside of you and me. A single protein molecule or a single fingerprint, a single syllable on the radio or a single idea of yours, implies the whole historical reach of stellar and organic evolution. It is enough to make you tingle all the time.

And yet the pleasure of total awareness still remains incomplete unless it includes the personal as well, unless one plunges into human life with it also. The creative principle, the active potentiality is inside of him too; and her; and them. To be sensed, enjoyed, responded to: a sensitive, quivering, pregnant web of interrelations.

It is so easy, really, and so much fun. The friend whom you meet is ready to laugh and respond to you. The child who comes in is ready to imitate you and share your amusement. Yes, and even the enemy—had you ever thought of not baiting him but enjoying him in all his crotchety horror? The secretary, the policeman, the shopper, the competitor, they are all waiting to unfold to your active response; they are all hot and tired and insecure—And they probably like ice cream, too. One glance or

comment, yielding to that unspoken humanity, will make it
more communicative, more humorous, more bearable. Be simple,
be direct, be wholly here with them, as spontaneous as a child;
you will win and they will win. How? (Are you afraid of it?)
In variety, in sensing, in living.

Suppose the grandest eternity you can imagine: It can only
be made up of a long continuing moment of awareness of
totality such as you have right now at your senses' tips. Part of
the reason why our pleasure in the present falls short, and why
we keep striving for a future pleasure that never comes, is that
we do not savor the present totality as we might, the sensory
totality, the evolutionary and intellectual totality, and the human
totality and our acting part in it. Having eyes, we see not;
having ears, we hear not. The reward of learning to be aware is
not a postponed reward, something for that delayed eternity
that was supposed to come after death; it is an immediate reward in the evolving, eternal now.

Tingle and start here. Children will change for you, men and
women will respond to you, awareness will come flooding in.
The world balances on a point at the tip of your finger.

Our recent era of change may be converging within this generation to a unique historical transformation to a totally new kind of life.

The Step to Man

Change, change, change, continual change. This is the watchword of modern life. Not only have we adjusted to it, but many of us have begun to revel in it. Conservative scientists have predicted the end of change at various times, but they have always been proved wrong. It seems it must go on forever. In the last two decades, the changes have been coming faster than ever before. Planes have passed the speed of sound, bombs have become incredible and then incredible squared, men are in orbit; and here below, new countries have proliferated, television has become universal, and every corner of the world is in a state of ferment.

Yet it seems to me that the excitement of our changes and emergencies has led us to look at them on too short a time scale. Let us not view them through the eyes of the newsman with this month's crisis or the advertiser selling this year's cars or even through the eyes of the planner announcing development programs for 15 years ahead. Let us look at our changes under the aspect of history. Grandparents are still alive who saw the coming of the motorcar and the airplane. Let us look at least as far ahead, to the time when our children will be grandparents in the twenty-first century; or 100 or 500 years ahead of that—to a time, say, as far away as the Renaissance is today.

I think anyone who does this will soon realize that most of the dramatic changes that have characterized the twentieth century, like those in travel and communications and weapons, cannot possibly continue at the present rates for anything like these lengths of time. It becomes obvious that many of them must converge rather soon to various kinds of limits, so that these aspects of society must begin to take on much more stable forms.

Should it surprise anyone that there might be an end to structural change in society? A boy does not go on growing forever. He finally reaches manhood and stops—though his mature accomplishments are just beginning. Likewise if a world once becomes unified, by communication and travel and mutual danger, into one world, the situation must level off. What more is there to do in that direction?

Many of our important indices of technical achievement have been shooting up exponentially for many years, very much like the numbers in the biologists' colonies of bacteria, that double in every generation as each cell divides into two again. But such a curve of growth obviously cannot continue indefinitely in any field. The growth of the bacterial colony slows up as it begins to exhaust its nutrient. The exponential curve bends over and flattens out into the more general "S-curve" or "logistic curve" of growth. Stevan Dedijer of the University of Lund, and Derek DeSolla Price have recently emphasized that research-and-development expenditures in the United States are now slowing up their rate of growth in just this way and are already beginning to be "past the middle of the S-curve." The reason is clear. Big research-and-development depends on big money, and these expenditures are beginning to exhaust their nutrient.

But I think this phenomenon of slowing up is now becoming much more general. Many scientists seem to suppose that we are just at the beginning of a curve of indefinitely accelerating change. They point out that Laplace and then Michelson long ago predicted the end of change in physics and that they were wrong. But it is one thing to see a slowing up of intellectual returns in certain areas, and another thing to see that life is short and the world is small and that there are physical and natural and economic limits to everything. I think it can be shown that many of our present changes are already rushing rapidly toward such limits. And many of our social adjustments to change are well on their way to what might be called "steady-state forms" that could accommodate orders of magnitude of further technical development without much additional restructuring.

I suggest that it is time to consider a different view, that we are not at the beginning of continually accelerating change, but that we are in the middle of a unique transitional crisis, like adolescence, as we make the jump from an undeveloped scientific and technological society to a fully developed one. Who knows?—we may be even beginning to be past the worst of the crisis, at least in countries like the United States. The slowing down of growth and the beginnings of our adjustment to it may become one of the major social phenomena of the next 30 years. Do you doubt this? Take a brisk excursion with me through some of our important areas of change and see if it is not so.

PLATEAUS IN SCIENCE AND TECHNOLOGY

Consider, for example what is happening at present in certain technical fields, as typified, say, by the high-energy accelerators of modern physics. DeSolla Price shows in his book that for 35 years now, we have been increasing the energies of our largest accelerators almost exponentially, as Fermi pointed out some years ago. It is worth quoting some of the numbers, although very approximate figures will suffice for the points I want to make. In the late 1920's, atomic particles could be accelerated to roughly 500,000 electron-volts of energy. Successive inventions raised the limit to about 20 million electron-volts in the 1930's; to 500 million by about 1950; and to 30 billion by the 1960's. Today, one machine under construction is designed for 50 billion electron-volts. This is an increase by a factor of 100,000 in energy—a factor of 10^5—in these 35 years, or a multiplication of the energy by another factor of 10 in every seven years.

Can new inventions raise the energies by still another factor of 10^5 in the next 35 years? Perhaps, but many doubt it. The reason is money. At present there are plans for a 200-billion-electron-volt accelerator, "the largest basic science project ever contemplated"; and then talk of a 1,000-billion-electron-volt machine. But this would be so large that it might require international cooperation to finance, and the work of thousands of physicists and engineers for 10 years to construct—that is, a major fraction of all the money and effort likely to be spent on physics in the whole world in that period. There are protests from other scientists whose projects are equally in need of money. Loud objections are being heard not only in scientific societies but in the halls of Congress.

Of course, this probable leveling off of one expensive field does not mean that the era of change is over, even in physics. Other areas of exponential progress may appear again and again. But this example shows us what forms and limits, from now on, will shape them all. Research and development is now a major social business, to be planned for, to be encouraged more richly than ever, to be put to immediate use when possible—and to be consciously limited to a fraction of the national resources and the national budget that is probably not far above the 20 billion dollars, or 3 per cent, that is presently being spent on it in the United States. There is a plateau here, an organizational steady state, that we have nearly reached already.

Let us go on to consider another rapidly changing technical field and one with more social impact, the field of computing machines. In the last 20 years or so, the 10-place desk calculator has been surpassed first by John von Neumann's ENIAC computer at the end of the war and now by much faster and more sophisticated devices. It is hard to give exact figures for the improvement in speed and capacity of the machines in this period because the principles of operation have changed drastically, but it might be estimated as a factor of roughly 10^5. In one instance that I know of, a brilliant student in the early 1950's took two years on a desk computer to do a quantum-mechanical calculation that was done five years later on an electronic computer in 14 minutes. By now, the time required to do this calculation, once a machine has been programmed for it, is probably less than one minute.

Today the designers of solid-state and other advanced computers say that a further increase in speed and capacity by a factor of 10 or 100 is in sight, but they do not seem to expect another factor of 10^5 in the next 20 years. When the information travels between the parts of a computer with the velocity of light, the natural limit to the speed of operation has been reached and this is a limit which is no longer very far off.

It is true that we are probably on the verge of great developments in applying computers to pattern perception and learning and to complex manipulating systems. But computers are already an integral part of advanced science, business, and government. Machining, accounting, management, and strategy problems are increasingly being turned over to them. It is, therefore, a little hard to see how even a dramatic extension of their powers could make as much further difference to our attitudes and ways of life as their development up to the present level has already made.

This may possibly be true even of the application of computers to automation, which is threatening to give us leisure in the decade ahead. This is sure to produce in the long run a great social restructuring; yet it is a restructuring which is already well under way. The problems produced by the elimination of labor are not the problems of the 30 hours a week, or 10 hours, or none, that a man works. They are problems of coupling this to economic distribution and to self-respect, and problems of idleness and boredom in the 138 or 158 or 168 hours when he does not work. They are not nearly as different from the present situation as it is different from that of the last century; and the time when we will be forced to find some sort of solution to these problems is almost certainly within the next decade or two. On the scale of history, are we not almost there already?

PLATEAUS IN COMMUNICATION AND TRAVEL

Suppose we turn instead to the fields of communication and travel. In communication, the coming of the telephone and radio and of television in the last 20 years—now with satellite relays across the oceans—has taken us onto a plateau that is obvious to anyone who thinks about it. Once we can transmit sight and sound around the world within two seconds whenever we want to, there is little left to be done but to extend the networks.

It is not generally realized, however, that we are also approaching an effective plateau in our speeds of travel. I once had the idea that we ought to organize a centenary celebration in honor of the occasion when man first traveled faster than the top speed of any animal or bird. This important breakthrough in evolution must have occurred just about 100 years ago when the steam locomotive first got up to 60 or 70 miles an hour.

Today, millions of people fly at 600 miles an hour in commercial jets. Commercial supersonic transports that will fly at 2,000 miles an hour are on the drawing boards; and experimental rocket planes have passed 4,000 miles an hour.

How long can this acceleration of speed go on? This is an easy question to answer, because it is finished. At around 100 miles an hour, we give up land transport and take to the air. At around 17,000 miles an hour, we give up air travel because we are in orbit. And this step is already behind us.

As a matter of fact, I think the full sociological consequences of high-speed transport are already implicit in the jet plane speeds we have today. Scarcely a hundred years ago, going around the world meant months of sailing around the Horn. Now civilians as well as armies can reach almost any point on the globe in less than a day. Can any further reduction in this time, say to six hours by supersonic transport, or to one hour by rocket, ever make as great a difference again? I think not. In most worldwide plans and operations, travel time is no longer the most significant variable.

Once horses had been tamed, men built their lives and societies around them for thousands of years. Today the United States is built around high-speed powered transportation. We have the automobile, the airplane, and the Go-Kart. It is transport that shapes the layout of roads and cities and airports and the structure and mobility of youth and workers and families and business and government. Might not our accommodations to fast easy transportation, and our attitude of taking it for granted, go on again almost unchanged for hundreds or thousands of years? I must confess that I fail to see how any new vehicle, no matter how marvelous, could again have the revolutionary effect that the railroad, the automobile, and the airplane had when they displaced the horse and carriage. Once more, regardless of future developments, in some important sense we are there already.

It is more surprising to realize that this is also almost true of space travel today, even though at the time I am writing this, it has been just seven years since the first orbiting satellite, *Sputnik,* was sent up. Dramatic order-of-magnitude improvements, manned missions to the moon and planets, and wonderful decades or centuries of exploration are still ahead. But the moon has already been photographed from close range and the Mariner flights are under way, sending back detailed data from Venus and Mars. Rockets already have the speed needed for exploring the solar system, and the times required would not be appreciably reduced by new plasma or nuclear rockets. The unexpected result is that the level of accessibility of the solar system that we can develop in the next 10 or 20 years may quite possibly represent its level of accessibility for hundreds of years to come.

Or to come back to terrestrial matters, consider the exploration of our own globe. Just since 1953, men have climbed the highest mountain and reached the bottom of the deepest sea. They have lived on a floating island in the Arctic and at the South Pole all year around—with running water and hot showers. Much more remains to be done, especially in exploring the oceans and penetrating the solid crust, but it is clear that the whole surface of the earth has become ours to study and use as we wish. When there is no farther to go, there is no farther to go. We have stepped up onto that plateau as well.

DANGER AND THE LIMITS OF DANGER

What about our technical achievements having to do with life and death?

I think the same imminent leveling off can be seen here also. As everyone knows, bombs have increased in power from the 20-ton chemical "blockbuster" of the early 1940's to the 20,000-ton atomic bomb at Hiroshima and then the 20-million-ton hydrogen weapons after 1953—an increase by six orders of magnitude within a single decade. Today the largest hydrogen bombs are equivalent to about 100 million tons of TNT, and there are so many of them—so much "overkill"—that they could wipe out all life on the planet. But the largest ones are already too large to have maximum efficiency for surface destruction, and the use of a number of smaller ones is computed to be more "effective" for military purposes. Will we make larger bombs in the future? We can if we want to, but even for the most overwhelming military purposes, we do not need to.

Even in the matter of the *control* of nuclear weapons, I think we may be approaching some sort of limit. This takes a little explanation. How dangerous can the situation get? At the present time we are near the edge of a precipice. Every year or two there is some major international crisis where there is a serious probability of an "accident" that could trigger a nuclear war and escalate into nuclear catastrophe for the world. Korea, Suez, Berlin, Quemoy, Cuba, Vietnam. Last week's crisis, whatever it was. It is nuclear roulette, so to speak, where the probability of a fatal shot may be small each time you pull the trigger, but where, if you play the game long enough, it finally, certainly, kills you. Dedicated men have worked very hard in each of these confrontations to avoid a nuclear incident, but we may not continue to be so lucky. Next time it may be a nuclear terrorist or a suicidal maniac or just a junior officer beyond control.

As a result, some have estimated that our "half-life" under these circumstances—that is, the probable number of years before these repeated confrontations add up to a 50–50 chance of destroying the human race forever—may be only about 10 to 20 years. Obviously this is not an objectively testable number. Nevertheless the idea is clear. We see that our boasted decreases in death rates and increases in the length of individual human lives in this century are spurious, as long as this nuclear danger is so uncontrolled. This is the first time in the history of the human race that babies—all babies everywhere forever—have had such a slim chance of survival.

Then why do I say that we are near a limit in these dangers? Just because this cannot continue. No one lives very long walking on loose rocks at the edge of a precipice. Either very soon, in 10 or 20 years, or in 30 or 40, we fall over the nuclear precipice;

or else very soon, before that time runs out, we argue some sense into our collective heads and move back from the danger.

Some talk of another possibility, that we might have a nuclear war with some people still surviving—at least *this* time—by going underground, in shelters and mines. But this, even if it could work, is only a temporary and horrible postponement of the problem—like falling partway down the precipice and then getting up, battered, to fall again. Do we come out of the shelters at last, to bury and clean up and rebuild, only to have the survivors going underground again with a resurgence of nuclear powers in another 20 years or so? And then again 20 years after that? Or do we stay underground for a thousand years and hope we will mysteriously have learned how to solve the problem of our competing nuclear threats after that time?

This is obviously not an alternative at all. It is nothing but a refusal to face the necessity for agreeing eventually on a method of international nuclear control. A refusal to see that no postponement in the shelters offers anything but greater danger and difficulty.

I have gone into these alternatives here simply to explain the basis of my conclusion that within a few years the situation will be over. Either we will be finished—or half-finished, trying to drag ourselves up again with none of the problems solved—or we will have drawn back from the precipice by actually bargaining or paying for nuclear restraints, with even the most difficult nations, so as to give us all a longer half-life.

But if in this short time ahead we can find a way to reduce these crises and probabilities by, say, a factor of 10, then we might begin to have 100 or 200 years to think how to reduce them further. And then we might begin to have a chance of lasting 2,000 years—or 20,000!—hopefully, say, as long as agriculture has lasted! I can only conclude that if we live, and if we work to live, we are even now within sight of a plateau and even a falling-off in the dimension of terror. But time is running out, and it is the wisdom and effort of men today, in this present generation, within the very next few years, that will make this permanent decision for us as to whether we live or die.

LIMITS OF DISEASE AND POPULATION

Finally, let us consider that other problem of life and death, the population problem.

Julian Huxley once pointed out that the two major biological inventions in historic times have been the control of germ diseases, and artificial contraceptives. They date from the work of Pasteur and of Goodyear just a hundred years ago. It is these inventions and their successors that are mainly responsible for our present population explosion—and for the hope of controlling it. They are the positive and the negative feedbacks determining human numbers.

Today bacterial diseases are approaching extinction, and virus diseases are coming under control. In the last 20 years, four of the last great killers, malaria, syphilis, tuberculosis, and polio, have been essentially wiped out, thanks to penicillin and sulfa drugs and vaccines and DDT. Cancer and circulatory diseases remain—and let no one belittle them! But most of mankind has already acquired toward disease the Pasteurian attitude, one that we might keep for a thousand years or forever, the attitude that we can do something about disease and need not remain its helpless victims.

The trouble is that this has led to an exponential growth of population that looks overwhelming unless something is done about it. And once more we discover that this present age is the time of the transitional crisis. It is said that paleolithic man doubled his numbers every 30,000 years. Today the world population doubles every 30 or 40 years—roughly 1,000 times as fast.

This exponential growth is so steep that it cannot go on for very long, on the scale of history. Today, our population is over 3 billion. By the year 2000, with a 40-year doubling time, it will be 6 billion; by 2040, 12 billion; by 2080, 25 billion; by 2120, 50 billion. This is almost 20 times our present numbers—a horrible prospect—and close to the estimated limit of the earth's food supply, even at the starvation level. But if the food supply is twice or four times as great, it is only a matter of another 40 or 80 years. The problem is in the exponential character of the growth, not in any particular numbers we put in. We see that within an uncertainty of 50 years or so, the time before the population growth slows up or levels off from starvation is only a couple of long lifetimes, a time no greater than the age of the United States. In fact, the famine is beginning already, with the population going up and the amount of food per capita now dropping steadily year after year in several countries.

If the world wanted to level off its population at some less extreme density before reaching universal starvation, say at a density of no more than twice our present numbers, we see that it would have to get agreements and apply effective methods of control almost immediately, for it would have to produce a leveling off in less than 40 years. The surprising thing is that this may now be technically possible, because of the rapid development of cheaper and simpler methods of birth control, such as oral contraceptives and intra-uterine coils, in the last decade. The problem is orders of magnitude easier than was believed even five years ago. The setting of birth rates and growth rates for a country is ceasing to be a matter of individual expense and resistance and is becoming a question rather of public policy and persuasion and effort. It is becoming a matter for conscious decision rather than collective drift. The widespread acceptance of this attitude in all countries and all religions is another plateau-step that may be taken in the very near future.

A CULTURAL SHOCK-FRONT

I have taken pains to enumerate these many areas where our civilization is beginning to be "past the middle of the S-curve," just because it is not generally appreciated how numerous and how central they are, or how convincing the evidence is that there are limits in sight. I realize that prediction is uncertain and that my conclusions are novel, but I think they are at least as plausible as the uncritical assumption that changes like those of the twentieth-century will go on forever. Marvelous developments lie ahead, particularly in biology, but I do not think they will make as radical a change in world society, as it is now being restructured, as the changes of the last hundred years made in nineteenth-century social systems.

If this is true, the present generation is the hinge of history. It may be no accident that the approach to maturation in

different fields shows a concurrent pattern. Our new developments in power and communication and control all support
each other. And they are supporting and being supported by the
simultaneous changes in economic and social and international
structure. It is those aspects of technological change that have
been pressing humanity so rapidly toward becoming a closely
interconnected species, a species in full possession of the world
and its abundance and with an adequate capacity for control
and survival, that are reaching toward mature and stable forms
in this generation. They are forms totally different from those of
our tribal warring past, but they might conceivably go on as long
as the old forms did, for hundreds or thousands of years into the
future. What is happening is that we are in the midst of being
compelled to reorganize the internal structure and powers of
the race into a mature human integration that could be called
manhood.

As a result, I think we may now be in the time of the most
rapid change in the whole evolution of the human race, either
past or to come. It is a kind of cultural "shock-front," like the
shock-fronts that occur in aerodynamics when the leading edge
of an airplane wing moves faster than the speed of sound and
generates the sharp pressure wave that causes the well-known
sonic boom. The front edge of this pressure wave is the shock-
front. It is a thin region where the low temperatures and
pressures of the air ahead of the plane change suddenly to the
high temperatures and pressures of the air immediately behind.

I think our present transitional crisis is a similar shock-front
for the human race, buffeting us about as sudden changes in
every direction come thick and fast. It is a multiple shock-
front, with each type of exponential change reinforcing all the
others. The Western world has encountered this cultural shock-
front first—it is closer to the airplane of history, so to speak—but
it would seem from the speed of industrialization of Japan and
Russia that the rest of the world can be no more than 30 or 40
years behind. Throughout the world, the farm and city ways of
historic man are being transformed rapidly to the ways of a
high-technology world society.

LIFE AHEAD

But the shock-front analogy is also an instructive way of thinking about the times ahead. It suggests that after the shock-front has passed, we will have reached larger powers and inter-actions—higher temperatures and pressures—but that the buffet-ing of change will be reduced, and the times will perhaps be-come psychologically and socially calmer than anything this generation or this century has known.

Life will go on being different partly for the familiar reason that we will go on having more population and power, more communication and science, in every decade. But it will also be different in a different way, because the approach to a steady state is something rare in the history of the world. We see that humanity is on the verge of a new kind of life. I think an examination of the question of what it will be like could be one of our most constructive intellectual exercises today. It would show us how different our present problems and solutions appear, when seen in the perspective of the great changes and the different structures just ahead. It would help us see what we must do to make the changes less traumatic and to shape the structures more intelligently.

The problem of arms control, for example, becomes a different problem if it is seen as a temporary substitute for other ways of keeping the peace in a disarmed world. Innovations in education take on a different character when seen as part of the total improvement in education that will be needed for every child in the world in 50 years. The need for philosophical integration of our new knowledge about the biological, intellectual, and social nature of man takes on great urgency when it is realized that this is the substructure on which the social and political philosophy of our grandchildren's world must be built. Where are our Montesquieu and Rousseau today? What have Freud and the behaviorists taught us about irrationality and educability that would help us design a good society, and a free and flexible society without the danger of recurrent instability? Are many different good societies possible, and can we choose among them or move at various times from one to another?

These are problems for extensive debate, but even without answering them it is easy to show that life in any steady-state world must differ in many respects from ours.

One of the unexpected differences, for example, will be the difference in age distributions and probably a related difference in family patterns. Throughout history, children have been a majority in most societies. The proportion of children to total population was high because so many were born who did not live to adulthood. It is estimated that at most times and places, half the population has been under age 15. Today in America, because of our postwar baby boom, half the population is still under 20. This makes a large "teen-age market" that many manufacturers are now trying to reach.

But in a steady-state world—no matter whether it has a smaller population than ours or one many times larger—the same number of people would be born in every decade and the same number would die in every decade. If our death rate in early life continues to go down, there will then be just as many people at age 40 or at age 60 as at age 10. And if they all live to about 80, as it now seems they might, then half of then will be over 40 and only one-fifth of them will be children under 15. It will be very different from the Indian village or the slum neighborhood with children everywhere underfoot. The curiosity and laughter of children will be scarce, and the world will begin to be run, even more than it has been, by the old.

A strange world for us. But it could be a good world, if the old remain young in heart and vigor. They could use their great excess of adult power, prosperous and leisured, to make the richest education for children that the world has ever known. Perhaps childless adults will move in with family groups, so they can share in the love and laughter of the children and spend endless hours in teaching them, in something like the old Hawaiian tradition. We may move away from our small-family separateness and back toward more tribal groupings as children become scarcer, and as the reduction of the speed of change makes it easier for the different generations to talk to each other again.

THE QUALITY OF LIFE

What will we do with our time in that leisured world? Undoubtedly there will be still more travel and more vigorous and daring outdoor recreation. Life will be dull otherwise. Perhaps thousands will climb Everest and millions will ride dolphins. But I think the activities that will really begin to bloom are the creative arts, education, and science. Not just Sunday painting, but Wednesday-Thursday-Friday-Saturday-Sunday painting. Continual rebuilding of your own home to your own taste, filling it with personal ingenuities and bold designs, might become the fashionable thing to do.

And education and science may become activities for everyone. Who kept up with the philosophers of the French Enlightenment? The leisured classes of the drawing rooms. Who did science at first? Rich amateurs and leisured clerics with an easy routine and the time to do experiments. Already education and scientific research are our fastest-growing industries. With preschool enrichment raising the level of intelligence, as some evidence now indicates, perhaps increasing numbers will profit from education all the way to the graduate level, and continuing education for much of the population may become a lifelong activity.

Likewise in science, many adults may fix up a laboratory room in their houses, where they can work every day at some scientific project, some study in crystallization or embryology, or in teaching animals, that could offer a lifetime of unfolding discovery.

One other characteristic of a steady-state world that deserves special mention is its requirement for a high standard of social justice. If we survive at all, after this great disturbing shock-front has faded into a phenomenon of history, it can only be by working out a new attitude of tolerance and mutual support for each other, between colored and white, between rich and poor, between advanced nations and retarded ones. The unemployed, the underprivileged, the underdeveloped, all the groups neglected or exploited by our present arrangements or condemned to exclusion from our prosperity by the accident of parentage or place of birth, form a perpetual seedbed for spokesmen and would-be dictators whose juntas may take over nuclear administration in the name of correcting these wrongs. Our failure to eradicate these evils depresses the standard of living and shortens the probable "half-life" of everyone. We are now realizing this, in Congress as well as in the councils of the world. What is fortunate for us today is that our new understanding of the educational and developmental basis of prosperity has made it possible and profitable to cure these evils just at the instant when our new weapons technology has made it absolutely necessary to do so.

We can no longer afford poverty in the world—if we ever could. We can no longer afford ignorance or prejudice or neglect. It is not so much that they are a sign of moral wickedness as that they are a sign of incompetence in design and administration. It is time to apply at least the same standards of competence and satisfaction in running the world that we apply in running a family or a business. Any member of the world now not only deserves to be shown, but must be shown, as surely as a member of a rich man's family, how he can share in its abundance. Any child in the world now not only deserves to have an education, but must have an education, like a privileged child, for the full development of his potentialities from the age of one year on up. It is necessary not only because we can afford it but because we must afford it.

The world has now become too dangerous for anything less than Utopia.

NEW KNOWLEDGE AND NEW BIOLOGY

Will it all be static in this strange new world of the steady state? The answer is no, nothing will be static. What will begin to be steady is our acceptance of these new ways of creative leisure and interaction as being the most interesting and most satisfying ways of life. But all our indices of flow, production, commerce, communication, will be up from what they are now. The marvelous accomplishments of a mature and integrated society will be just beginning. And two fields, scientific knowledge and biological technology, will surely go on changing and developing indefinitely.

I see no end to the increase of knowledge. When scientific research has as many men and as much money every year as society can afford, it will be adding even more rapidly than now to our knowledge of nature and to the ease with which we can control nature. And this world of nature is infinite to us, for it includes the human brain itself. After all the myriad galaxies of the astronomers are charted as well as we want to chart them, we will still go on studying the multimyriad complexities of the brain that has measured them.

Our knowledge of nature will surely be used increasingly for the improvement and variation of our biological apparatus for living. If we can actually set up a social structure that will enable us to live together without killing ourselves, for a thousand years or a million years—a time as long as the time since man began—it will begin to give us the time we need to understand and develop our full biological potentialities. Things we now cut out of the human body by surgery—the appendix, the tonsils—can they be eliminated from the hereditary genes instead? Our eyes and ears that give out when we are old, our hearts and arteries, why not make them better biologically from the beginning rather than by doctoring after they begin to fail? We begin to see the possibility of reshaping the human organism, as we have been reshaping plant and animal organisms now for many years, into a new form or into many new forms that will begin to show the full potentialities of protoplasm and the creative brain. In such a time, man will cease to be at the mercy of the evolutionary accidents that made his frame and his society—just as he has ceased to be at the mercy of the biological accidents that made his diseases. It will be a time when man can begin to plan what he wants man to be, as each individual makes his personal plans today—a time when accident and drift will finally begin to be replaced by conscious human values and decisions.

METAMORPHOSIS

The accelerating powers and dangers and hammer-blow stresses of these days make us anxious and afraid. But I think it is clear that if we survive this shock-front, this roaring waterfall of change, we could be within sight of what Churchill once called the "sunlit uplands."

Various metaphors could be used to describe the situation. In many ways, it is like a child learning to ride a bicycle. There you were, up until that day, riding on the three-wheeler where you couldn't hurt yourself very much. But then you get the two-wheeler, and it seems terribly scary, and perhaps you fall and skin a knee or an elbow. But you get up again, and your father holds the handlebars running along beside you, and suddenly you are riding alone. At one instant you are incompetent, falling to one side or the other and steering wrong, and the next instant it comes right and you are in control, safe and balanced not because you are fearful and slow but because you are going faster than ever. Wobbling and weaving but nevertheless choosing your *own* path and balancing safely at every turn. So, I think, in 30 or 40 years, if we survive, the human race will come through this time of wobbling conflict and uncertainty and falling, and will suddenly be riding in its own chosen direction, free, as only a coordinated and confident organism can be.

To say it another way, it is like the time of adolescence, when the teen-ager suddenly changes, with some thrashing about, from the dependent child to the independent man. Or it is like the moment of birth, full of pain and danger as the baby in the womb is suddenly pushed through into a new life where he must breathe alone and learn to walk and talk and think. Or it is like the moment of metamorphosis of the insect, when there is an incomprehensible swelling and dizzy changes of shape and desire in the tight cocoon, until suddenly it bursts open at the end of its own sharp S-curve, its own era of change, to reveal an unimagined transformation to a new free winged life.

This is the meaning of the leveling off of our S-curves. We are now nearing the end of the era of change. We have been isolated human beings, selfish, combative, ignorant, helpless. But now for several hundred years the great evolutionary hormones of knowledge and technology have been pressing us, almost without our understanding it, into power and prosperity and communication and interaction, and into increasing tolerance and vision and choice and planning—pressing us, whether we like it or not, into a single coordinated humankind. The scattered and competing parts are being bound together. Everywhere now we begin to see men and nations beginning the deliberate design of development with a growing confidence in the choice and creation of their own future. The exponential changes have burst apart our ancient attitudes and structures, and our failure to adjust to this may yet kill us, but if we are wise and energetic and understand our own nature and purposes well enough to restructure and control these dangers, mankind may emerge very quickly into coordinated forms such as it has never known before. Our drastic changes will not go on forever. They are converging to a limit. It was implicit in the biological material all along, as surely as the butterfly is implicit in the caterpillar. We have been men. We are emerging into Man.

Yet no analogy, not even that of metamorphosis, quite captures the suddenness and radicalness, the really complete restructuring, of the transformation ahead. If the two billion years of life are represented by that 200-foot height of, say, the Rockefeller Chapel at Chicago, the million years of man make a one-inch block on top of the chapel. The 20,000 years of agriculture make a thick postage stamp on top of that, and the 400 years of science make the ink on top of the postage stamp. Now, suddenly, we see what all this has been building up to; and it is about to come within a single generation or two—that is, in the thickness of the film of moisture on top of the ink on the postage stamp. In that short time we will move, if we survive the strain, to a wealthy and powerful and coordinated world society reaching across the solar system, a society that might find out how to keep itself alive and evolving for thousands or millions or billions of years, a time as long as all of evolution past. It is a tremendous prospect. Hardly anyone has seen the enormous sweep and restructuring and unity and future of it except perhaps dreamers like H. G. Wells or Teilhard de Chardin. It is a quantum jump. It is a new state of matter. The act of saving ourselves, if it succeeds, will make us participants in the most incredible event in evolution. It is the step to Man.

Notes and References

Where Will the Books Go?

1 "Microbooks" is a trademark copyrighted by Microbooks, Inc., of Milwaukee, Wisconsin. The term as used in this chapter, however, does not refer to their particular (and interesting) commercial products, but uses the prefix "micro" only in the scientific sense of "one-millionth," to refer to a whole class of possible books reduced in physical size by about this factor compared to ordinary book sizes.

2 R. P. Feynman, *Engineering and Science (Caltech)* 20, 20–25 (February 1960).

3 Since the original magazine publication of this chapter, a system like this has come on the commercial market. This is the "Photo-Chromic Micro Image (PCMI)" system of the National Cash Register Company of Dayton, Ohio, and it offers a reduction of about 220 times in linear dimensions or 48,000 times in area. At this Company's exhibit at the New York World's Fair in 1964, contact prints of the Holy Bible at this scale were available, with the 1,245 pages of the Bible printed into less than two square inches. The text was sharp and easily readable at the magnification of an ordinary biological microscope. This is not quite as great as the scale of reduction whose potentialities are explored later in this chapter, but it would make it possible to have a library of all the world's books on one wall of an office, and it demonstrates the feasibility of the ideas outlined here and how close their implications are to realization.

4 Direct electronic storage of books—without printing—either on magnetic tape or on computer drums is now, in 1966, much more feasible for large libraries than it was when this chapter was written. Some enthusiasts think that the new "time-sharing" systems will make it possible to store all recorded information in a big computer serving a network of consoles in many cities, and that this will be a much faster and better solution to the indexing and retrieval problems than any photographic microstorage. See J. C. R. Licklider, *Libraries of the Future* (M.I.T. Press, 1965). However, the photographic microlibraries discussed here could be available many years before complete computer libraries, and would long continue to be valuable for private individuals or for underdeveloped countries that were not connected to the computer network or could not afford the computer terminal costs; and their images could be "read into" local television systems in just the way described.

Strong Inference

[1] A. M. Weinberg, *Minerva*, Winter 1963, p. 159; also in *Physics Today* 17, 42 (1964).

[2] G. Polya, *Induction and Analogy in Mathematics* (Vol. 1) and *Patterns of Plausible Inference* (Vol. 2) (Princeton University Press, Princeton, N.J., 1954).

[3] J. R. Platt, *The Excitement of Science* (Houghton Mifflin, Boston, 1962). Especially Chs. 7 and 8.

[4] J. D. Watson and F. H. C. Crick, *Nature* 171, 737 (1953).

[5] M. Meselson and F. Stahl, *Proc. Natl. Acad. Sci.* 44, 671 (1958).

[6] A. Rich, in *Biophysical Science: A Study Program*, Eds. Oncley et al. (John Wiley, New York, 1959), p. 191.

[7] S. Benzer, *Proc. Natl. Acad. Sci.* 45, 1607 (1959).

[8] J. Lederberg, *Science* 129, 1649 (1959).

[9] P. F. Davison, D. Freifelder, and B. W. Holloway, *J. Mol. Biol.* 8, 1 (1964).

[10] R. L. Garwin, L. M. Lederman, and M. Weinrich, *Phys. Rev.* 105, 1415 (1957).

[11] W. A. H. Rushton, Personal communication.

[12] See G. F. Chew, M. Gell-Mann, and A. H. Rosenfeld, *Sci. Amer.* 210 (2), 74 (Feb. 1964); 210 (4), 60 (April 1964); 210 (6), 54 (June 1964).

[13] F. Bacon, *The New Organon and Related Writings* (Liberal Arts Press, New York, 1960), esp. pp. 98, 112, 151, 156, 196.

[14] K. R. Popper, *The Logic of Scientific Discovery* (Basic Books, New York, 1959), p. 41. A different view is given by T. S. Kuhn in *The Structure of Scientific Revolutions*, University of Chicago Press, 1962, but does not, I believe, invalidate any of the conclusions given here.

[15] T. C. Chamberlin, *J. Geol.* 5, 837 (1897); (reprinted in *Scientific Monthly*, Nov. 1944). I am indebted to Professors Preston Cloud and Bryce Crawford, Jr., of the University of Minnesota for correspondence on this article and a classroom reprint of it.

The interest aroused by the present chapter when it first appeared in *Science* led to a reprinting of the Chamberlin article in that Journal (*Science*, May 7, 1965), as suggested here. It has also been reprinted in pamphlet form by the Institute for Humane Studies, Inc., Stanford, California, and copies are obtainable from them for fifty cents each.

[16] M. Faraday, *Faraday's Diary 1820–62* (G. Bell and Sons, London, 1932–1936).

[17] H. L. Anderson and S. K. Allison, *Rev. Mod. Phys.* 27, 273 (1955).

[18] E. C. Watson, *Am. J. Phys.* 13, 281 (1945) gives an English translation of both of Roentgen's first papers on X-rays.

[19] See G. W. Wheland, *Advanced Organic Chemistry* (John Wiley, New York, 1949), Ch. 4, for numerous such examples.

[20] B. K. Forscher, *Science* 142, 339 (1963).

Seed Operations

[1] Mathematical equations for the chain-reacting aspect of the growth of pre-war belligerence between opponents were first given and graphed, it

seems, by Lewis F. Richardson. See his posthumous books, *The Statistics of Deadly Quarrels* and *Arms and Insecurity* (Quadrangle Books, 1960).

2 Alice Kimball Smith, "The Elusive Dr. Szilard," *Harper's Magazine* 221 (No. 1322), pp. 77–86, July 1960.

3 Eugene Rabinowitch, "James Franck 1882–1964 and Leo Szilard 1898–1964," *Bulletin of the Atomic Scientists*, October 1964, pp. 16–20.

Limits, Balance, and Guidance in Society

1 Since this chapter was written, two major books emphasizing the feedback approach in political science have been published by my colleague, Prof. David Easton: *A Framework for Political Analysis* (Prentice-Hall, 1965), and *A Systems Analysis of Political Life* (John Wiley and Sons, 1965).

2 My friend Arthur H. Mankin, an electrical engineer very much interested in the political process, first pointed out to me in the early 1950's the majority-election theorem described here and its game-theoretical explanation. Some of these conclusions have now been examined more extensively by Dr. Anthony Downs in his book *An Economic Theory of Democracy.*

3 This idea for the self-refunding and profitable support of education by Educational Investment Corporations has recently been discussed a little more extensively by Prof. Richard L. Meier in his book, *Developmental Planning* (McGraw-Hill, 1965).

4 For a more extensive discussion of the present American incentives for population reduction, see John Rader Platt, "The Delicate Question of Population," *The New Republic* 139, No. 2232, Sept. 2, 1957, pp. 11–14.

The Federalists and the Design of Stabilization

1 A somewhat different version of these requirements and their possible solutions will be found in Alexander Rich and John R. Platt, "On Keeping the Peace in a Disarmed World," a paper given at the 10th Pugwash conference on Science and World Affairs, London, 1962; to be published in *Bulletin of the Atomic Scientists* (1966).

Changing Human Nature

1 Originally given as the Phi Beta Kappa address, Brandeis University, June 1962.

Index

Perspective, long-range, effect on present problems, 197
Philosophical basis of future society, 197
Photo-Chromic Micro Image (PCMI) System, 6
Physics, high-energy, 24
Pinhead library, 5
Planning the future, 165–166
difficulties of, 82–83
Plasticity of behavior, 160–161
Plateaus, in communication and travel, 189
in science and technology, 187
Platt, J. R., 21, 206, 207
Point Four Program, 44
Polya, G., 21, 206
Popper, Karl, 27, 206
Population growth, as a chain-reaction, 41, 74
control, 43
incentives for control, 104–105
necessary leveling off, 194–195
Positive feedback, 43
Prediction, as goal of science, 141
Price, Derek de Solla, 54, 186, 187
Printing, history of, 8
Privacy-indeterminacy, 147
Probability and unpredictability, 143
Problem-oriented social inventions, 134
Proportional representation, 50–51, 93
Psychology, of a culture, 90
Publication policies in science, 65–66
Punishment versus reward, in political design, 118–119, 122

Qualitative issues, 33
Quality of life, 202–203
related to age-distribution, 198
Quantum effects in vision, 147
"Question, The," 35

Rabinowitch, Eugene, 84, 207
Rational planning, 116–117

Rationing coupons, as feedback systems, 46
as a medium of exchange, 104
Reaction-times, in science, 65
Reading rate, 13–15
Realism and goodness, 103
Reorganization of human race, 196
Representation, in a disarmed world, 127
Research and development for social problems, 132ff
Response as a tool in shaping behavior, 180
Revenue for an international organization, 125–126, 135–136
Rewards, individual, and social goods, 101ff, 105
Rich, Alexander, 22, 207
Richardson, Lewis F., 206–207
Richelieu, Duc de, 78
Ripley, George, 160
Roentgen, Wilhelm, 30
Ruml, Beardsley, 44, 77, 133
Rushton, W. A. H., 25
Russell, Bertrand, 154–155
Ryo-Nen, 182

Sale, compared with compromise, 103
Schrödinger, Erwin, 33, 152
Science and art as everyday hobbies, 199
Science departments, size effects, 60–62
Science, method-oriented versus problem-oriented, 21
Scientific approximations, effect on philosophy, 154–155
Scientific inference, steps in, 20
Scientific research, need for protection, 67
value of supporting services, 68
Scientists, numbers in different fields, 66
value to nation, 67
Second Law of thermodynamics, 152
Security barriers, 60